It's another Quality Book from CGP

Want to hear the **bad news**? There's an awful lot of heavy stuff
you need to know for GCSE separate sciences.

Want to hear the **good news**? Good old CGP have got it all covered!
We've produced this brilliant book with all the concepts
beautifully explained in clear, simple English so
you can understand it — and remember it.

And then, in the spirit of going the extra mile, we've put in
a smattering of not-so-serious bits to try and make the
whole experience at least partly entertaining for you.

We've done all we can — the rest is up to you.

What CGP is all about

Our sole aim here at CGP is to produce the highest quality
books — carefully written, immaculately presented and
dangerously close to being funny.

Then we work our socks off to get them out to you
— at the cheapest possible prices.

Contents

Published by: Coordination Group Publications Ltd

Contributors: Taissa Csáky
Charley Darbishire
Chris Dennett
Sandy Gardner
Dominic Hall
Gemma Hallam
Jason Howell
Sharon Keeley
Simon Little
Tim Major
Andy Park
Glenn Rogers
Julie Schofield
Claire Thompson
James Wallis

ISBN 1 84146 215 2
Groovy Website: www.cgpbooks.co.uk

Printed by Elanders Hindson, Newcastle upon Tyne.
Clipart sources: CorelDRAW and VECTOR.

Pathogens — Bacteria and Viruses

Q1   What is a pathogen?

Q2   Name four kinds of micro-organism that can act as pathogens.

Q3   Are all ~~pathog~~ens parasites?

Q4   It hasn't always been generally accepted that disease and decay were caused by living organisms.
   a)   What did people think caused things to go off and go mouldy?
   b)   Describe Pasteur's experiment on flasks of broth. What did he conclude?

Q5   Sketch the diagram of a bacterium on
   the right, and label parts **W**, **X**, **Y** and **Z**.

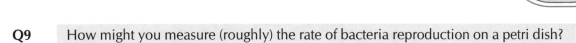

Q6   How do bacteria reproduce?

Q7   How many chromosomes does a bacterium have?

Q8   How does a flask of broth with bacteria growing in it look
   different to a flask of broth with no bacteria growing in it?

Q9   How might you measure (roughly) the rate of bacteria reproduction on a petri dish?

Q10   How do bacteria survive dramatic changes in environmental conditions
   (e.g. extremes of temperature or pH)?

Q11   Sketch this diagram of a virus, and label parts **A** and **B**.

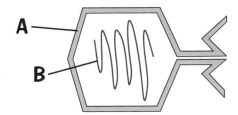

Q12   Which life processes do viruses not carry out?

Q13   Describe the way in which viruses use a host cell to replicate themselves.

Pathogens — Fungi and Yeast

Q1   What is a mycelium?

Q2   Sketch this diagram of a fungal hypha.

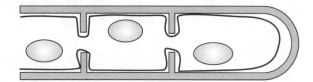

    a)   Label the hyphal membrane, hyphal wall, cytoplasm and nuclei.
    b)   Why is the membrane in the diagram above not called a cell membrane?

Q3   Sketch a diagram of yeast, and label the nucleus, cell membrane and cell wall.

Q4   How does yeast reproduce?

Q5   Give the word equation for anaerobic respiration in yeast.

Q6   Match the diagrams 1, 2 and 3 to the descriptions a, b and c.

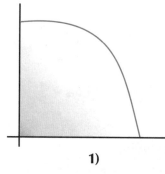   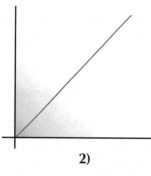   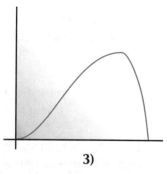

          1)   **2)**   **3)**

    a)   Rate of bacteria/fungi reproduction against amount of food available.
    b)   Rate of bacteria/fungi reproduction against temperature.
    c)   Rate of bacteria/fungi reproduction against amount of toxic waste products.

Q7   Name a disease caused by each of the following:
    a)   Bacteria
    b)   Fungi
    c)   Viruses.

Top Tips...

You've got four different kinds of pathogen to learn about. These questions will test if you actually know the facts. Watch out for the little details about structure and reproduction of these little blighters. You don't want to be caught out when the Exam comes round.

The Spread of Disease

Q1 Give one example of a disease spread via each of the following:

    a) the air
    b) water
    c) contaminated food
    d) body contact
    e) insect

Q2 What is a disease vector?

Q3 What two organisms are involved in the spread of malaria?

Q4 Give a definition for each of the following:

    a) endemic disease
    b) epidemic disease

Q5 What impact does easy global travel have on the spread of disease?

Q6 Copy and complete the following passage using words from the box below.

education	airborne	unprotected sex	sneezed	vaccination
	bodily fluids	breathing in		needles

> Influenza is an _____ virus. It is spread by _____ viruses from the air that have been _____ out by an infected person. A _____ is now available each year against the most common form of the virus.
>
> HIV can only be spread by the transfer of _____. The virus is most commonly transferred during _____ and the sharing of _____. The spread of HIV is mainly fought by _____.

Q7 What disease does HIV cause, and what are its symptoms?

Q8 How do each of the following factors affect the spread of disease?

    a) Availability of clean water.
    b) Availability of proper sanitation and sewers.
    c) Availability of good food.
    d) Education, literacy and the percentage of children who go to school.
    e) War.

Q9 For each of these parasites, say how people become infected, and give one way in which they can avoid infection.

    a) Toxocara.
    b) Head lice.
    c) Tapeworm.

Section One — Disease and Micro-organisms

Making Stuff Safer

Q1 Disinfectants and antiseptics can be used to kill many pathogens.

  a) Give an example of a disinfectant and say what it is used for.

  b) Give an example of an antiseptic and say what it is used for.

  c) What is the difference between a disinfectant and an antiseptic?

N.B. Chlorine dissolves lycra

Q2 How might each of the following be sterilised?

  a) A swimming pool   **b)** Surgical instruments   **c)** Food

Q3 Give brief details of the flash pasteurisation process for milk.

Q4 The water from our taps is treated to make it safe to drink.
Put these stages of treatment in the right order:

  chlorination   filtration   sedimentation

Q5 Look at this diagram of a sewage treatment works, and label parts A, B and C.

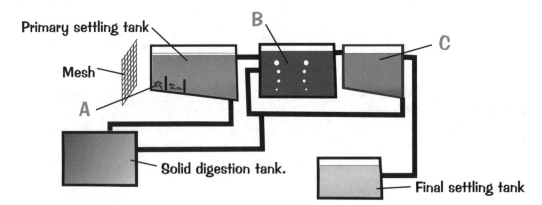

Q6 In the primary settling tank of a sewage works,
what rises to the top, and what sinks to the bottom?

Q7 Solids from the primary settling tank are transfered to the solid digestion tank for treatment.

  a) What is added to the solids from the primary settling tank to digest them?

  b) Under what conditions does this digestion happen, and how long does it take?

  c) What gas is produced?

Food Poisoning

Q1 Salmonella is a bacterium that causes food poisoning.

   a) Name another pathogen that causes food poisoning.

   b) In what temperature conditions does Salmonella reproduce fastest?

   c) What harmful effects does Salmonella have on the human body?

   d) How does it produce those effects?

Gas mark 7, licence to grill

Q2 Why is it important to make sure that the fridge is at a cool temperature?

Q3 Why must uncooked meat be kept on the bottom shelf of the fridge?

Q4 Chickens bred intensively for meat are kept in sheds which are cleaned out very rarely, if at all. Why might Salmonella bacteria be more common in meat from intensively farmed chickens than in meat from free-range chickens that roam free in fields?

Q5 Say whether each of these food preparation practices is safe or unsafe. If the practice is unsafe, explain why.

   a) Using a fork to beat eggs, scrambling the eggs and then using the same fork to eat the eggs.

   b) Using different chopping boards for meat, vegetables and cheese.

   c) Wiping a chopping board with a damp cloth after using it to cut up meat.

   d) Scrubbing a chopping board in hot soapy water after using it to cut up meat.

Q6 Mayonnaise made from eggs that might be contaminated with Salmonella is irradiated to kill all micro-organisms. Someone who eats the mayonnaise still gets ill with food poisoning symptoms. Explain how this can happen.

Q7 Explain how the following methods of food preservation prevent dangerous levels of micro-organisms:

   a) canning

   b) freezing

   c) drying

   d) ultra-heat treatment

Q8 For each of the food preservation methods in Q7, give an example of a food that's preserved in that way.

Top Tips...

Well, if that's not enough to put you off scrambled eggs for life, I don't know what is. You need to make sure you can remember all the safe practices for handling food — and, just as important, <u>why</u> they're safe.

Defence Against Disease

Q1   Name two different kinds of white blood cell, and describe the special functions that they have.

Q2   What is an antigen?

Q3   Copy and complete the following passage using the words on the right.

> _____ and _____ lymphocytes make up the immune response.
> _____ have receptors on their surface which recognise particular _____.
> These cells then _____ the pathogen which contains that _____.
> _____ secrete antibodies. When an antigen has been detected, these
> cells _____ to make lots of identical cells secreting identical _____ to
> fight the infection.

antigens   B-type
multiply   T cells
T-type   B cells
antibodies
destroy   antigen

Q4   A person is infected by a pathogen and their antibody levels are recorded. Next year the person is infected with the same pathogen. Again antibody levels are recorded. The graph on the right shows antibody levels during the two infections.

    a)   Does the person get as ill following the second infection as they do following the first infection?

    b)   Why are the levels of antibody in the blood so much higher 8 hours after the second infection than they are 8 hours after the first infection? (Refer to the type of white blood cell responsible for this.)

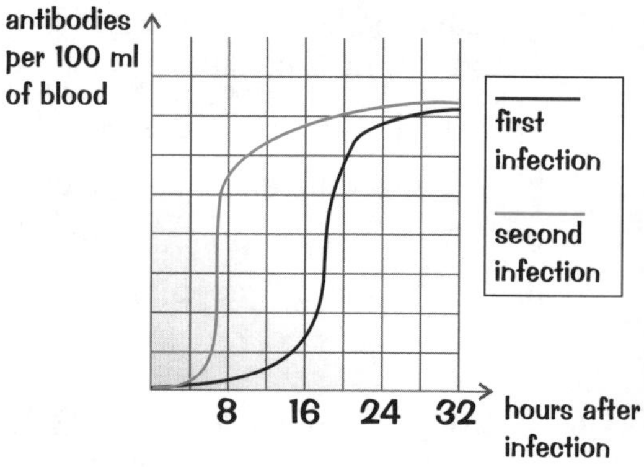

antibodies per 100 ml of blood

first infection

second infection

8 16 24 32 hours after infection

Q5   Vaccination protects against viral diseases.

    a)   Give an example of a vaccination given to young children to protect them against common diseases.

    b)   Which diseases does this vaccination protect against?

Q6   The "flu jab" is a vaccination against the influenza virus.

    a)   What is injected into the body in this vaccination?

    b)   How does the body react to this?

    c)   How does this prevent the vaccinated person from becoming ill with flu?

    d)   The influenza virus changes and mutates each year. Explain, in terms of antibodies and the body's immune response, why the "flu jab" does not give life-long protection against influenza.

Q7   What are monoclonal antibodies?

Q8   Describe how mouse cells and tumour cells are used to produce monocolonal antibodies.

Q9   How is breast milk beneficial to the immune system of a new born baby?

Antibiotics

Q1 Give an example of a medicine that does not cure disease, but only relieves the symptoms.

Q2 Give an example of a medicine that does cure disease.

Q3 Are ant█████s effective against diseases caused by viruses?

Q4 Why is it difficult to kill viruses without damaging the body's own tissues?

Q5 The first antibiotics to be discovered were penicillins.

    a) What organisms naturally produce penicillins?
    b) How were penicillins discovered? Who discovered them?
    c) Who found out how to purify penicillin?
    d) When was the drug first produced industrially and used on a large scale?

Q6 Copy this diagram of an industrial fermenter used to make penicillin. Label the arrows (1-7).

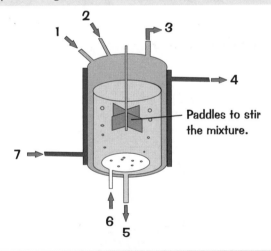

Paddles to stir the mixture.

Today you're getting mould therapy followed by cheesy foot sniffing ... all better soon.

Q7 Say why each of the following parts of the fermenting process to make antibiotics is necessary.

    a) Providing food through an inlet pipe.
    b) Bubbling air through the mixture.
    c) Allowing gases to escape though an outlet pipe.
    d) Using a water cooled jacket around the fermenter.

Q8 How do bacteria become resistant to antibiotics?

Q9 Give two ways in which the risk of antibiotic resistance is increased.

The Blood, the Brain and Reflexes

Q1   What are the four main blood groups?

Q2   Copy this table and fill in the gaps.

Blood Group	Antigens	Antibodies
A	A	
B		anti-A
AB		
O		

Q3   Blood contains antigens (A, B, both or neither) and antibodies (anti-A, anti-B, both or neither).

a)   What component of the blood carries the antigens?

b)   What component of the blood carried the antibodies?

c)   What happens when B antigen meets anti-B antibody?

Q4   For each of the following blood groups, say which blood groups they can get transfusions from and which blood groups they can give transfusions to:

a)   Group A   **b)**   Group B   **c)**   Group AB   **d)**   Group O

Q5   Why is a constant blood pressure important for the kidneys?

Q6   Why is a constant blood pressure important for the brain?

Q7   Sketch this diagram of the brain.

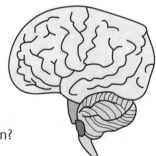

a) On your diagram, lable:
  i)   the cerebrum,
  ii)   the cerebellum,
  iii)   and the medulla.

b) What are the roles of these three parts of the brain?

Q8   Sketch this diagram of a reflex arc, and label the dorsal root, ventral root, and grey matter.

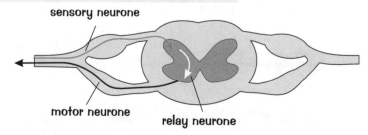

sensory neurone

motor neurone

relay neurone

Section One — Disease and Micro-organisms

Kidney Disease

Q1   What is the role of the kidneys?

Q2   What happens when the kidneys don't function properly?

Q3   How is ▮▮▮y disease treated on a week by week basis?

Q4   How can kidney disease be cured?

Q5   During dialysis, waste products are removed from the blood into dialysis fluid across a differentially permeable membrane.

    a)   What's the name for this process?

    b)   What would happen to the glucose in the blood if there was no glucose in the dialysis fluid

    c)   What would happen to the water levels in the blood if the concentration of the dialysis fluid was too weak?

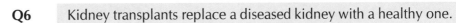

Q6   Kidney transplants replace a diseased kidney with a healthy one.

    a)   Can kidneys be transplanted from living donors?

    b)   Why is it important get a donor kidney which matches the patient's tissue type?

    c)   The patient's white blood cell production is temporarily stopped. What could the white blood cells do if their levels were normal?

    d)   How is white blood cell production stopped?

    e)   Why must a transplant patient be kept in sterile conditions after the transplant operation?

Q7   What is the organ donor register?

Q8   Give advantages and disadvantages of dialysis.

Q9   Give advantages and disadvantages of kidney transplant.

Top Tips...

All you need to know about what the kidneys do and how they do it is in the Double Science Biology revision guide. These questions are about what happens when kidneys go wrong, and to be honest, they're not that hard. You could get asked about kidney transplants, so learn the details.

Growing Micro-organisms

Q1   What is a culture medium?

Q2   What nutrients do micro-organisms need to grow?

Q3   Use the words from the box to label the diagram.

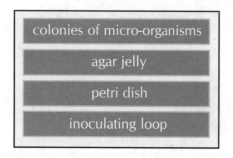

| colonies of micro-organisms |
| agar jelly |
| petri dish |
| inoculating loop |

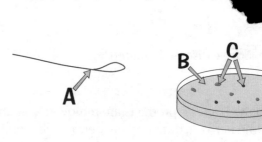

Q4   Equipment used to handle and grow micro-organisms is sterilised.

   a) What would happen if the equipment was not sterilised?

   b) How are inoculating loops sterilised?

   c) What are inoculating loops for?

   d) Why do petri dishes need lids?

Q5   Write out the passage below, choosing the correct response from the brackets to complete it.

> In school labs, micro-organisms are grown at about [**8 °C / 25 °C / 50 °C**].
>
> This is not [**warm enough / cold enough / wet enough**] for
>
> [**micro-organisms / harmful pathogens / hippopotamuses**] to grow.
>
> In industrial conditions, micro-organisms are grown at [**lower / cooler / higher**]
>
> temperatures so that they grow much [**faster / slower / prettier**].

Q6   Give four advantages of using micro-organisms for food production.

Q7   Say whether each of the following sentences is true or false.
Rewrite correctly any sentences which you think are false.

   a) Mycoprotein means "protein from mould".

   b) A fungus called *Fusarium* is the main source of mycoprotein.

   c) Mycoprotein is used to make egg substitutes for vegetarian meals.

Top Tips...

There isn't much here that's too confusing. There are a few bits of jargon that might be new, like
"culture medium" and "inoculating loop", but they don't mean anything desperately complicated.
All you need to do is work on the questions until you get them all right.

<u>Micro-organisms in Food Production</u>

Q1 During the production of cheese, bacteria form a solid in the milk. This solid is then separated from the liquid.

   a) What is the solid part called?

   b) What is the liquid part called?

   The solid is then pressed and left to ripen.

   c) What is ⬛ added to the solid at this stage?

Q2 What kind of micro-organism is responsible for the veins in blue cheese?

Q3 Copy and complete the passage below. Use the words from the box.

> germinate   sugar   barley   malting   wheat   ear wax
>   dried   cooled   alcohol   yeast   starch   hops

Beer is made from grain. The most common type of grain used is _____. The grain
is allowed to _____ for a few days before being _____ in a kiln. Enzymes break
the _____ in the grains down to _____. This process is called _____.
The sugary solution is fermented by _____. This turns the sugar into _____.
_____ are then added to give the beer a bitter flavour.

Q4 Put these stages of the process to make soy sauce in the right order.

The mixture is fermented by yeast.

The mixture is pasteurised.

The mixture is fermented by *Lactobacillus* bacterium.

The mixture is fermented by *Aspergillus* fungi.

The mixture is filtered.

Cooked soy beans are mixed with roasted wheat.

Q5 Why must soy sauce be bottled in sterile bottles?

Q6 Micro-organisms can contaminate food, causing food poisoning. List three rules which should be followed to reduce this risk.

NB: Chickens should have feathers, not fur. (especially not blue fur).

Micro-organisms in Industry

Q1 Identify three useful products from the list below
which are made from micro-organisms on a large scale.

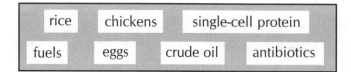

rice	chickens	single-cell protein
fuels	eggs	crude oil	antibiotics

Q2 Read the following statements about industrial micro-organism
production using a fermenter. Say whether each statement is
true or false. Correct the sentences which you think are false.

   a) The culture medium is a solid.

   b) The food for the micro-organisms is contained in the air.

   c) The pH inside the fermenter must be carefully monitored.

   d) It doesn't matter what temperature it is inside the fermenter.

   e) Air is piped in to supply carbon dioxide to the micro-organisms.

Q3 *Fermenters are usually cooled by water.
What is making the fermenter heat up?*

Q4 What type of cells can single-cell proteins be made of?

Q5 Write out this passage, choosing the correct word or phrase from the brackets.

Due to the [**rapid population growth** / **population decline**] in some developing countries, the
[**GDP** / **demand for food**] is very high.

The climate in these countries may fail to support animals. Because animals are a very good
source of [**protein** / **carbohydrate** / **fibre**], an alternative source is needed. [**Single-cell protein** /
Penicillin] is one possible alternative because it is [**efficient** / **expensive**] to produce.

Q6 Penicillin is an antibiotic made by growing *Penicillium* in a fermenter.

   a) What type of micro-organism is *Penicillium* — bacteria, fungi or mould?

   b) Does *Penicillium* start to make penicillin as soon as it is put in the fermenter?

Top Tips...

Well, this isn't exactly the most exciting stuff on the planet. But anyway, you've got to know how to
keep micro-organisms happy on a large scale. It's like having a tank of goldfish — if you don't give
them the right stuff they drop dead on you. Actually, not so much drop as float to the surface.

Fuels from Micro-organisms

Q1 Fuels can be made by a natural process using micro-organisms.
What is the name of this process?

Q2 Ethanol can be made from glucose using yeast.

   a) Copy and complete this word equation:

| | | Ethanol | + | | (+ | energy |) |

   b) Waste from which industry is often used to produce ethanol?
   c) What can ethanol be used for?

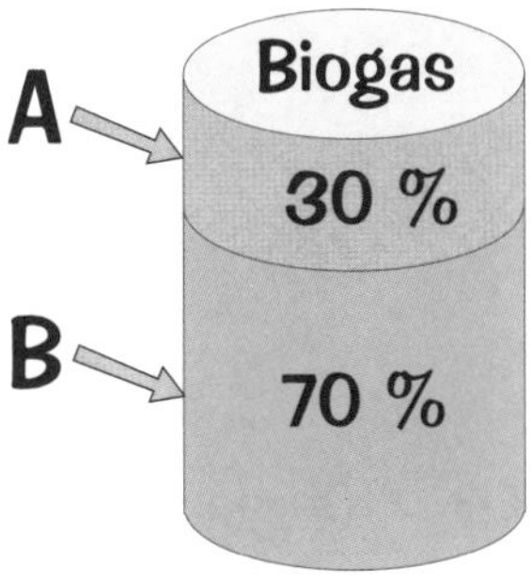

Q3 Identify the main components of biogas in the diagram on the right.

Q4 What raw materials can biogas be made from?

Biogas

A → 30 %

B → 70 %

Q5 Give four uses of biogas.

Q6 Why does biogas have to be used straight away? Choose your answer from the four below:

   a) It smells too bad.
   b) It can't be stored as a liquid.
   c) It is highly explosive.
   d) It is always needed.

Q7 The following sentences refer to either "batch" or "continuous" digesters.
Make a table with two columns labelled "batch digesters" and
"continuous digesters". Write each sentences in the appropriate column.

   a) Make biogas in small batches.

   b) Waste is continuously fed in.

   c) Make biogas at a steady rate.

   e) More suited to large scale projects.

   d) Manually loaded up with waste.

   f) By-products are cleared away at the end of each session.

Q8 Biogas can be generated on a small scale to
provide energy for a household or a village.

Biogas
is ace

   a) What kinds of waste are used to generate biogas on a small scale?
   b) What can the by-products of biogas generation be used for?

Manipulating Reproduction

Q1 What are clones?

Q2 Use the words from the box to fill in the gaps in the description of mammal cloning below.

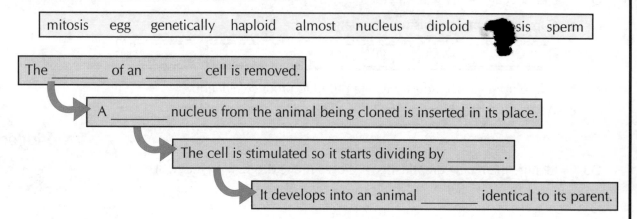

| mitosis egg genetically haploid almost nucleus diploid ~~osis~~ sperm |

The _____ of an _____ cell is removed.

A _____ nucleus from the animal being cloned is inserted in its place.

The cell is stimulated so it starts dividing by _____.

It develops into an animal _____ identical to its parent.

Q3 Do cloned embryos usually develop normally?

Q4 Explain why people are concerned about cloning.

Q5 *Stem cells are cells that can grow into all kinds of specialised cells, e.g. liver cells and kidney cells.*

If a patient needed a liver transplant, why would it be better to clone his stem cells and use them to grow liver cells rather than to use a liver from a donor?

Q6 Decide whether each of these sentences about cattle reproduction in intensive farming are true or false. Write a correct version of each sentence you think is false.

a) Ovulation is artificially controlled.
b) The biological father of the calf actually mates with the biological mother.
c) Bull semen is stored in a warm place.
d) Fertilisation takes place inside the biological mother.
e) A surrogate mother carries the calf and gives birth to it.

Q7 Why are surrogates used in the breeding of cattle? (Hint: think about ovulation and pregnancy.)

Q8 What is the main problem with selective breeding?

Top Tips...
If you remembered the stuff about cattle reproduction you can have a pat on the head. This stuff about cloning sounds like science fiction — an army of super-human clones might take over the planet. Or perhaps they will start cloning pop stars and we can all have our own Michael Jackson.

Gene Technology

Q1   Briefly describe the structure of DNA.

Q2   Who were the X-ray diffraction photographers whose work showed Watson and Crick what the structure of DNA was?

Q3   What type of bond joins nucleotides of DNA together?

Science teachers might think this gag is funny. Everyone else reacts as if they'd just eaten six lemons.

Q4   *Each nucleotide contains a base.*

   a) What are the four bases in DNA called?
   b) The bases always pair up in the way. Which bases pair with wich?

Q5   Copy out the following paragraph and fill in the gaps.

DNA carries the code for making _____. Proteins are made from long chains of _____ _____. Each _____ _____ is coded for by a set of _____ bases. A set of bases that makes up the code for one amino acid is called a _____.

You're big enough and clever enough to work out for yourself what goes in the gaps.

Q6   The DNA code is transferred onto messenger RNA.

   a) Describe how this happens.
   b) What's the name for this process?
   c) Where in the cell does this process occur?
   d) Where in the cell are proteins made?

Q7   Look at the diagram on the left showing a piece of RNA.

   a) What kind of RNA is this?
   b) What role does it play in the synthesis of proteins?

Q8   Sometimes, mistakes happen in copying DNA to RNA.

   a) What's the technical term for this?
   b) The copying mistake could be that a base is missed out of the RNA.
       Give two other examples of possible mistakes in copying the bases of the DNA code.
   c) Name two things that make these mistakes more likely.

Genetic Fingerprinting

Q1   Give an example of a situation where a person's DNA is **not** unique.

Q2   Give two uses of genetic fingerprinting.

Q3   What ethical problems are raised by genetic fingerprinting?

Q4   DNA "fingerprints" are made by cutting a piece of DNA into bits, and seeing how long the bits are.

    a)   What is used to cut the DNA?

    b)   Explain why the DNA of one allele of a gene could be cut into lots of small bits, while a different allele of the same gene gets cut into fewer bits.

    c)   How are the big bits of DNA sorted out from the smaller bits?

Q5   A gene for a human protein X is isolated from a sample of human DNA. It's spliced into a loop of bacterial DNA, and the bacteria are grown in a fermenter.

    a)   What do you eventually get out of the fermenter?

    b)   Give an example of an important hormone that is made in this way.

    c)   Why are bacteria used to make proteins like this?

Q6   Some bacteria containing the gene for a genetic disease are grown in a petri dish. A piece of fabric is used to pick up bacteria from the surface of the dish. A test piece of DNA that's complementary to the gene is added to the fabric.

    a)   What is meant by the term "complementary" in this context?

    b)   Some of the test DNA sticks to the fabric. Why?

    c)   What's the fancy name for the test piece of DNA?

    d)   Describe how X-ray or UV light is used to see the test DNA.

Top Tips...

There's a lot of tricky details in this biotechnology section — and you really need to sit down and learn them all. These questions should help. Make sure you know the simple bits first, then learn all the fiddly details like <u>protein synthesis</u> and <u>genetic fingerprinting</u>. Don't get caught out in the exam.

Agriculture and the Environment

Q1   Choose the substance below that's most likely to solve each of the agricultural problems (**a-e**).

a) Most of the minerals have been removed from the soil.

b) The soil is too acidic.

c) Greenfly are eating the crops.

d) Weeds are competing with the crops.

e) The soil is too alkaline.

Q2   Describe one problem that can be caused by the use of inorganic fertilisers.

Q3   Gertrude decides to test the pH of the soil in her garden. It is a dry, sunny day.
She places a strip of pH paper on the soil but nothing happens.

a) Give one reason why Gertrude might want to know what the pH of the soil is.

b) What would be a better method to find out the pH of the soil?

Q4   Complete the paragraph below by choosing the correct words from the box.

> minerals   plants   gravel   rock   oxygen   balance
> greenhouses   carbon dioxide   environment   water

Hydroponics is where _____ are grown on a surface such as
_____ instead of soil. They are bathed with _____, and receive
the right _____ of dissolved _____ for healthy growth.
Growing plants in _____ speeds up photosynthesis. The warm, light
_____ is perfect for growing plants. To speed photosynthesis up
even more, extra _____ can be added.

Q5   Suggest three ways in which genetic engineering can improve food production.

Top Tips...

You never know when this topic will 'crop up'* in exams so make sure you know all about it. Really
efficient farming is a good thing generally, but try to remember the downside as well. All these
chemicals may make crops grow better, but they can cause environmental problems too.

Systems of Classification

Classification's all about naming living things. Rover, Fluffy, Homo sapiens...

Q1   What is meant by the term "species"?

It's Trevor, actually ...

Q2   Write down what is meant by:

a)   a natural classification system.

b)   an artificial classification system.

Q3   What did John Ray and Carl Linnaeus look at to help them decide how to classify plants?

Q4   Linnaeus's system for naming living things is called the 'binomial system'. Explain:

a)   what binomial means.

b)   what group the word *Homo* refers to in '*Homo sapiens*'.

c)   what group the word *sapiens* refers to in '*Homo sapiens*'.

Q5   How are each of the following creatures' names written in the binomial system?

a)   The lion (family *Felidae*, genus *Panthera*, species *Leo*).

b)   The house fly (order *Diptera*, family *Muscidae*, genus *Musca* species *Domestica*).

c)   The rainbow trout (family *Salmonidae*, subfamily *Salmoniae*, genus *Oncorhynchus*, species *Mykiss*).

d)   The African Clawed Frog (order *Anura*, family *Pipidae*, genus *Xenopus*, species *Laevis*).

Q6   What are the common names of each of these? *(If you're not sure — have a guess.)*

a)   *Felis catus*

b)   *Homo sapiens*

c)   *Canis lupus*

Q7   Give three reasons why people consider it important to conserve species.

Q8   What does species diversity measure? (Use words from the box to complete the sentences below.)

i)   The .... of different species in a habitat.

ii)   How many .... of each species there are in a habitat.

mass	individuals	diversity	number	types

Animals and their Breathing

Q1   These two feet are from different animals.

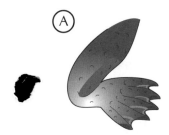 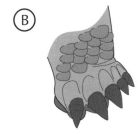

a)   Which foot belongs to a reptile? Give as many reasons as you can for your answer.

b)   Which foot belongs to an amphibian?   Give as many reasons as you can for your answer.

Q2   *To live fully on land, an animal must reproduce on land.*

a)   Describe the eggs of an amphibian.

b)   Describe the eggs of a reptile.

c)   Where must an amphibian reproduce?

d)   Do amphibians live fully on land? Explain your answer.

Q3   *To live on land, an animal must be able to breathe oxygen from the air.*

a)   How do fish take in oxygen?

b)   Can a fish take in oxygen when it is out of the water?

c)   How do adult amphibians take in oxygen?

d)   What happens to an amphibian when it is out of water for a long time?

e)   How does this restrict the areas where an amphibian can live?

Q4   Sketch this diagram of a fish and label parts A, B and C.

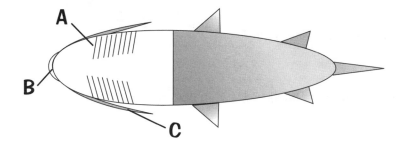

Top Tips...

Breathing — it's a useful skill. Fish and amphibians have very different breathing methods from other animals, and it's really important that you know what they are. You need to be able to say how a frog, or a fish, or a lizard is adapted to its environment — and go into a bit of detail about it too.

Vertebrates

Q1   What do vertebrates have that invertebrates don't have?

Q2   Classify the following as vertebrates or invertebrates:

    a)   eel   **b)**   wasp   **c)**   tarantula   **d)** chicken

    e)   earthworm   **f)**   sea snake   **g)**   vole

Q3   What is the function of the skeleton?

Q4   What has to happen for the bones at a joint to move?

Q5   For each of these diagrams, say what will happen to
the end of the bone, B, when the muscle, M, contracts.

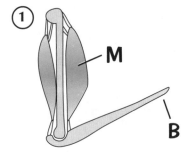 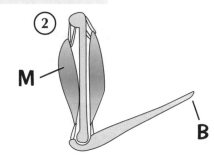

Q6   Look at this diagram of the bones and muscles at a joint.

    a)   What is part A?

    b)   What is part B, and what is it for?

    c)   What is secreted at C, and what does it do?

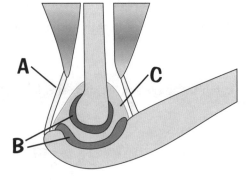

Q7   What stops bone from being brittle?

Q8   Why is it important for ligaments to have high tensile strength?

Q9   Why is it important for ligaments to have some elasticity?

Q10   Tendons have high tensile strength, but not much elasticity. Why is this?

Fish and Birds

Q1 Look at this picture of a fish.

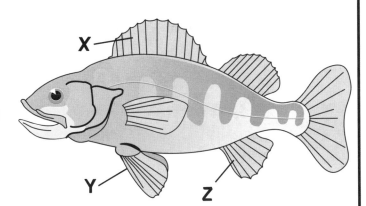

a) Give two ways in which is it adapted to its environment.

b) How does the large surface area of the tail help this fish to move in the water?

c) What is the purpose of the fin at X?

d) The fins at Y and Z are in pairs? Why is this?

Q2 Answer these questions about fish.

a) How does the zig-zag arrangement of muscles help fish to move through the water?

b) What is the function of the swim bladder?

Q3 What physical properties do the primary "flight" feathers on a bird's wings have that make them well adapted for flight?

Q4 How are a bird's bones adapted to suit flying?

Q5 How is a bird's body shape adapted for flight?

Q6 Look at this cross-section of a wing and answer the questions below.

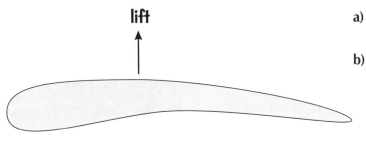

lift

a) What creates the lift that birds need to fly?

b) When a bird flaps its wings downwards, there are no gaps between the feathers.
When it flaps its wings upwards, there are gaps between the feathers. Why is this necessary?

Q7 Why does a bird need such a large sternum (breastbone)?

Q8 What bone structure did the bird's wing evolve from?

Invertebrates Feeding

Q1   Look at this diagram of a mussel.

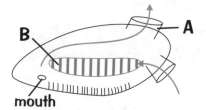

a)   What is the purpose of part A?

b)   Name part B. What gets trapped there?

c)   How does food get from part B to the mouth?

d)   What do the arrows represent?

Q2   *Mosquitoes feed on blood.*
Say how each of the following are adapted
to allow the mosquito to feed on blood.

a)   The mosquito's proboscis.

b)   The throat muscles.

c)   The saliva.

Q3   What parasite can mosquitoes carry in their saliva?

Insects feeding

Q4   *The parasite carried by mosquitos causes disease in humans.*

a)   Where in the human body does this parasite feed, grow and reproduce?

b)   What symptoms are caused by this parasite?

Q5   *Many insects feed using a proboscis.*

a)   How do aphids get their food into their mouths?

b)   Name two other insects that feed using a proboscis.

Q6   *An organism which undergoes metamorphosis*
changes its appearance completely over its life cycle.

a)   Describe the life cycle of a blow fly.

b)   What is one advantage of metamorphosis for the organism which goes through it?

Section Three — Adaptation and Evolution

Teeth

Q1   Look at these diagrams and then answer the question below.

Ⓐ

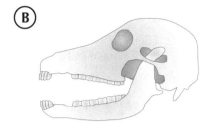

Ⓑ

a)   Which diagram shows the teeth of a herbivore? Explain your answer.

b)   Which diagram shows the teeth of a carnivore? Explain your answer.

Q2   This is a diagram of a human lower jaw.
For each type of tooth, A-D, write down what it's called and what it's for.

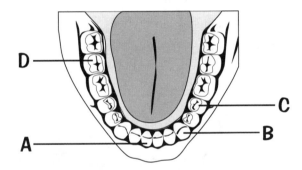

Q3   Answer the following questions about dog's teeth.

a)   How are a dog's incisors adapted to eating meat?

b)   How are a dog's canines adapted to eating meat?

c)   What is the name of the special large premolars that dogs
and other carnivores have?

d)   What are these teeth used for?

e)   Does a dog's jaw allow side-to-side movement, like a
human's jaw?

f)   Explain why your answer to part **e)** is an advantage to dogs.

Top Tips...
This is mostly basic stuff. The difference between herbivore and carnivore teeth, and the purposes of
the different kinds of human teeth is all old hat really. The only new things to learn are the special
features of carnivore jaws. So do the questions. They won't bite. Ho ho.

Section Three — Adaptation and Evolution

Digestive Systems

Q1   *Grass and leaves contain cellulose.*

    a)   Why does the digestive system of mammals have difficulty in breaking down cellulose?

    b)   What micro-organisms do sheep and cows have in their digestive system to make eating grass and leaves worthwhile?

Q2   *Cows' stomachs have four chambers called the reticulum, the rumen, the omasum and the abomasum.*

    a)   What happens to a cow's food before it enters the rumen?

    b)   What happens to a cow's food in the rumen.

Q3   *Rabbits do not have a rumen, but they do have an extra section in their digestive tract.*

    a)   Where is this extra compartment?

    b)   What does it contain?

    c)   Why is it that rabbits produce green faeces?

    d)   What do rabbits do with the green faeces, and why?

    e)   Copy out the diagram below and fill in all the labels.

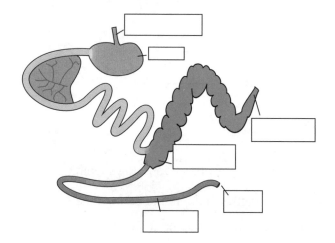

Q4   *Relationships like the one between mammalian herbivores and cellulose-digesting bacteria are described using the word "symbiosis" or "mutualism" — because the relationship's of mutual benefit to the bacteria and the mammals.*

    a)   What do the mammal herbivores get out of the relationship?

    b)   What do the bacteria get out of the relationship?

Q5   Do carnivore digestive systems have special sections for cellulose-digesting bacteria?

Exercise

Q1   What do muscle fibres do when supplied with energy?

Q2   What process provides this energy?

Q3   Copy out this diagram and fill in the gaps to show how substances
are supplied to and taken away from the muscles during exercise.

GLUCOSE and OXYGEN
supplied by the ....

⟶

MUSCLE cells convert
.... to ....

.... and ....
taken away by the blood

⟶

Q4   How do muscle fibres adapt to regular exercise?
What effect does this have on the body's appearance?

Q5   *Denise does not exercise regularly. After 15 minutes on a rowing machine, her arms and legs
feel stiff and sore. Danielle is in the habit of exercising for half an hour three times a week.*

   a)   After 15 minutes on a rowing machine, would you
expect Danielle's arms and legs to feel stiff and sore?

   b)   Explain your answer to a).

Q6   Explain how regular exercise benefits each of the following:

   a)   joints

   b)   lungs

   c)   heart

Q7   Look at this graph of pulse rate over
time, then answer the questions.

   a)   Which pulse rate is Danielle's?

   b)   Which pulse rate is Denise's?

   c)   Why does the pulse rate of both women
rise when they begin to exercise?

   d)   Explain the difference between the pulse
rate of the two women.

   e)   At what point was Danielle and
Denise's blood pressure highest?

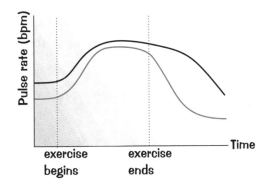

Q8   What's the difference between a sprain and a strain?

Q9   What's a dislocation? Where are dislocations most common?

Acids and Bases

These questions are about acids and bases... as if the page title wasn't enough of a giveaway.

Q1　What substance must be present for a substance to act as an **acid** or as an **alkali**?

Q2　Write down the ions on the right that are responsible for the following reactions:

a)　Reactions of an acid in aqueous solution.

b)　Reactions of an alkali in aqueous solution.

H^+　　OH^-　H^-　　OH^+

Q3　*Lowry and Brønsted defined acids and bases in terms of **proton transfer**.*

a)　Write down the Lowry-Brønsted definition of an **acid** in terms of transfer of protons.

b)　Write down the Lowry-Brønsted definition of a **base** in terms of transfer of protons.

Q4　*Acids and bases can be either **weak** or **strong**.*

a)　What is the definition of a strong acid?

b)　Give two examples of strong acids.

c)　What is the definition of a weak acid?

d)　Give an example of a weak acid.

Must...
increase...
concentration...

Q5　Which of the acids in each of these pairs is **stronger**?

a)　1 mol/dm^3 HCl (pH 0) and 1 mol/dm^3 HNO$_3$ (pH 1)

b)　1 mol/dm^3 CH$_3$COOH (pH 2.38) and 1 mol/dm^3 HCOOH (pH 1.87)

Q6　*1 g of magnesium ribbon fizzes vigorously for 3 seconds when dropped into 200 cm^3 of acid A.*
1 g of magnesium ribbon fizzes gently for 10 seconds when dropped into 200 cm^3 of acid B.

a)　Given that both acids are of the same concentration, which is stronger?

b)　If you didn't know that both acids were of the same concentration, would you be able to say which was stronger?

Q7　*Acids can be strong or weak — they can also be concentrated or dilute.*

a)　Explain the difference between saying an acid is strong and saying that it is concentrated?

b)　Is a dilute acid always weak?

Q8　Join up the scientists on the left with their ideas about acids and bases on the right.
(You don't need to use all the sentences on the right.)

Lowry and Brønsted

Arrhenius

Acids ionise to form H$^+$ ions and bases form OH$^-$ ions.

Acids release H$^-$ ions and bases accept H$^-$ ions.

Acids release H$^+$ ions and bases accept H$^+$ ions.

Solubility of Salts

These questions are about how well salts dissolve.

Q1 Write out these sentences, including the correct word(s) out of each pair in brackets.

Ionic compounds (**are** / **are not**) generally soluble in water.

Covalent compounds (**are** / **are not**) generally soluble in water.

Sodium, potassium and ammonium salts (**are** / **are not**) generally soluble in water.

Q2 Which of the following **nitrates** are soluble in water?

a) $Pb(NO_3)_2$ c) Barium nitrate   e) $Al(NO_3)_3$

b) $AgNO_3$ d) Magnesium nitrate   f) Iron(II) nitrate

Q3 Which of the following **chlorides** are soluble in water?

a) $CaCl_2$ c) $PbCl_2$ e) $AlCl_3$

b) Magnesium chloride   d) Potassium chloride   f) Copper chloride

Q4 Which of the following **sulphates** are soluble in water?

a) $CuSO_4$ c) $BaSO_4$ e) Ammonium sulphate

b) Aluminium sulphate   d) Lead sulphate   f) $CaSO_4$

Q5 Which of the following **carbonates** are soluble in water?

a) Sodium carbonate   c) $MgCO_3$ e) Copper carbonate

b) Barium carbonate   d) $(NH_4)_2CO_3$ f) $Fe_2(CO_3)_3$

Q6 Write out these sentences and fill in the gaps using words from the boring grey box.

| solute | saturated | increases | solvent | saturated | solute | salts | solute |

A solution is made up of a _____ dissolved in a _____. The solubility of most _____ increases as the temperature _____ . A _____ solution is one in which no more _____ will dissolve at that temperature. When a _____ solution cools, some of the _____ will crystallise out.

Q7 Look at this solubility curve for sodium nitrate, and use it to answer these questions.

a) How much sodium nitrate can be dissolved in 100 cm³ of water at 45°C?

b) A saturated solution of sodium nitrate is cooled from 50°C to 20°C. How much salt crystallises out?

Q8 *Artificial fertilisers contain ammonium and nitrate ions.*

Which property of ammonium and nitrate ions makes it easy for them to leach out of the soil into natural watercourses?

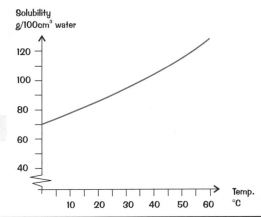

Solubility g/100cm³ water

120

100

80

60

40

10 20 30 40 50 60 Temp. °C

Making Salts

Any chemist worth their salt can do these questions.

Q1 Which of these is the most accurate definition of a salt?

> A compound containing one metal and at least one non-metal, joined together with covalent bonds.

> A compound containing one metal and one non-metal, joined together with ionic bonds.

> An ionic compound formed when an acid is neutralised by an alkali.

Q2 *Some salts can be made in the lab by a direct reaction between the elements that they're made up of.*

Care of Animals Rule No. 57: Never pour salt in a rabbit's eyes.

a) Give an example of a salt that can be made this way.

b) Describe the process used to make a salt in this way.

c) What safety precautions should you take when using chlorine gas in the lab?

Q3 Some salts are prepared by precipitation.

a) What is a precipitation reaction?

b) What is the product of the reaction between lead nitrate and hydrochloric acid?

c) Magnesium sulphate is insoluble. How could you make magnesium sulphate in the lab?

d) Write a balanced equation for the reaction in part **c)**.

Q4 *A salt and hydrogen are the products when a metal reacts with an acid.*

a) Write out a balanced equation for the reaction between zinc and nitric acid.

b) What happens when a piece of calcium is dropped into a test tube of dilute hydrochloric acid? Is it safe to carry out this reaction in the lab?

c) What happens when a piece of copper is dropped into a test tube of dilute hydrochloric acid?

Q5 *This question is about how metal hydroxides react with acids.*

a) Write a balanced equation for the reaction between iron hydroxide and hydrochloric acid.

b) Is this a neutralisation reaction, a displacement reaction or a precipitation reaction?

Q6 *Metal carbonates react with acids to produce carbon dioxide, water and a salt.*

a) Write a balanced equation for the reaction between zinc carbonate and nitric acid.

b) When reacting excess zinc carbonate with nitric acid, how can you easily tell when the reaction is finished?

c) How would you isolate a pure sample of the product?

Q7 *Sodium (Na^+), potassium (K^+) and ammonium (NH_4^+) salts are generally soluble in water.*

a) When reacting **solid** potassium carbonate with hydrochloric acid, why is it not easy to tell when you've added an excess of potassium carbonate?

b) Instead, a **solution** of potassium carbonate could be used. What method might be used to ensure that the right amount of potassium carbonate is added to neutralise the acid?

Gases: Solubility and Collection

Q1 How does the solubility of a gas change as the **temperature** increases?

Q2 How does the solubility of a gas change as the **pressure** increases?

Q3 *When the cap is removed from a bottle of fizzy drink, the drink fizzes up.*

   a) What gas forms the bubbles in the drink?

   b) Why do bubbles of gas appear when the cap is removed from the bottle?

Q4 *Rivers and lakes contain dissolved oxygen.*

   a) Why is this vitally important?

   b) What happens to oxygen levels when warm water is discharged into rivers?

   c) Where might this warm water come from?

Q5 Give two uses for chlorine water.

Q6 *Imagine that you're carrying out a reaction to generate a gas —
you're using a delivery tube and a gas jar to help collect the gas.*

   a) The gas is heavier than air. Describe how you would collect the gas.

   b) This time, the gas is lighter than air. Describe how you would collect the gas.

   c) Give an example of a gas which is lighter than air.

   d) Give an example of a gas which is heavier than air.

Q7 *Gases can be collected over water.*

   a) Copy the diagram and complete it to show a
   method of collecting gas over water.

   b) Which gases must not be collected over water?

   c) Why must these gases not be collected over water?

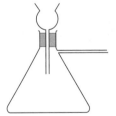

Q8 Match each gas to the way of testing for it. One has been done for you.

| Hydrogen | Oxygen | Carbon dioxide | Sulphur dioxide | Ammonia | Hydrogen chloride |

| Turns damp red litmus paper blue | Turns limewater milky | Turns damp blue litmus paper red | Turns damp orange dichromate paper green | Relights a glowing splint | Squeaky pop with lighted splint |

Q9 What are the potential hazards involved in making and collecting hydrogen?

Top Tips... The questions about gas solubility are fairly straightforward, but that's no excuse for not doing them. And when it comes to collecting gases, there are several different methods to remember. If you got stuck on any of the questions, you need to go back and learn the stuff again.

Tests for Positive Ions

If you want to identify unknown ionic compounds, you need to be able to test for various ions.

Q1 Name four positive ions that can be identified using a flame test?

Q2 Which ions produce the following colours in a flame test:
a) Orange?
b) Brick red?
c) Lilac?
d) Blue-green?

Q3 When sodium hydroxide (NaOH) is added to an unknown ionic compound, a coloured hydroxide may precipitate out. This can be used to identify the positive ion in the compound. Copy and complete this table to show what colour precipitate would form with these metal ions.

Metal	Ion	Colour of precipitate
Calcium	Ca^{2+}	
Copper(II)		Blue
Iron(II)	Fe^{2+}	
	Fe^{3+}	Reddish brown

Q4 How is the ammonium ion identified by reaction with sodium hydroxide solution?

Q5 An unknown solid is dissolved in water, and sodium hydroxide solution is added. A **white precipitate** forms. More sodium hydroxide is added, and the precipitate eventually **dissolves**. What is the **positive ion** in the unknown solid?

♫ Always look on the bright side of life...

Q6 Copy and complete this table showing the ionic equations for the reactions between hydroxide ions and the metal ion shown:

Metal ion	Ionic Reaction
Calcium, Ca^{2+}	
Copper, Cu^{2+}	
Iron (II), Fe^{2+}	
Iron (III), Fe^{3+}	
Aluminium, Al^{3+}	

Obvious joke no. 81432: Positive iron (ahem)

◄ Write the ionic equation for what happens when excess NaOH is added as well.

Top Tips... Flame tests and the sodium hydroxide test are all very well, but the real trick is learning the colours you get and what they mean. And the thing to remember about ionic equations is that they're 'half' a full equation — they just show the bit of the reaction you're <u>interested</u> in.

Section Four — Preparing and Analysing

Tests for Negative Ions

Q1   *Negative ions can sometimes be identified by their reactions with dilute acid.*

a)   What gas is produced when a carbonate reacts with dilute acid?

b)   What is the lab test for this gas?

c)   Give a balanced equation for the reaction between sodium sulphite (Na_2SO_3) and HCl.

d)   How do you test for the gas produced in this reaction?

Woke up this morning, got the iron blues.

Q2   *The test for sulphates involves a precipitation reaction.*

a)   Describe the test for sulphates.

b)   Write out a balanced equation for the ionic reaction in this test.

Q3   *The test for halides involves another precipitation reaction.*

a)   What acid is added to a solution of the unknown salt in the test for halides?

b)   What other reagent is then added?

c)   What colour is the precipitate formed by a chloride?

d)   What colour is the precipitate formed by a bromide?

e)   What colour is the precipitate produced by an iodide?

Q4   Write out this paragraph about litmus paper and fill in the gaps using the words on the right.

Litmus paper can be used to test for _____ and _____ ions. Blue litmus paper turns red if _____ ions are present — this means that the substance is an _____.

Red litmus paper turns _____ if _____ ions are present — this means that the substance is an _____.

alkali

OH^-

OH^-

blue

H^+

acid

H^+

Q5   *Ed is trying to identify an unknown solid. He gets negative results when he tests for carbonate, sulphite, sulphate, hydrogen, hydroxide and halide ions. He decides to test to see if the compound is a nitrate.*

Describe the test for a nitrate. You should say what reagents you'd use and what the expected product is.

Quantitative Chemistry

Q1   State Avogadro's Law.

Q2   What is the volume of the following gases at standard temperature and pressure (STP)?

a)   2 moles of chlorine   c)   4 moles of hydrogen

b)   2.5 moles of carbon dioxide   d)   1.5 moles of sulphur dioxide

Q3   How many moles are in each of the following at STP?

...and add a splash of CaSO₄, with a dollop of MgBr₂ and a dash of worcester sauce...

a)   6000 cm³ of carbon dioxide   c)   60 dm³ of oxygen

b)   18000 cm³ of nitrogen   d)   8 dm³ of carbon monoxide

Q4   Answer the following questions on volumes of gases in reactions.

a)   Hydrogen reacts with chlorine to give hydrogen chloride: $H_2 + Cl_2 \rightarrow 2HCl$.
What volume of chlorine reacts to give 18 dm³ hydrogen chloride (at STP)?

b)   Hydrogen reacts with nitrogen to give ammonia: $3H_2 + N_2 \rightarrow 2NH_3$.
If 4500 cm³ of hydrogen is used, what volume of ammonia is produced
(assuming that there's no excess of either hydrogen or nitrogen, and that all the
hydrogen and nitrogen is converted to ammonia)?

Q5   What's the concentration of a salt solution with 0.5 moles of salt dissolved in 250 cm³ of water?

Q6   Work out the concentration of the following solutions:

a)   40 g of sodium hydroxide (NaOH) in 500 cm³ of water.

b)   202 g of potassium nitrate (KNO_3) in 1500 cm³ of water.

c)   36.5 g of hydrogen chloride gas dissolved in 1000 cm³ of water.

Hint: work out the molar mass of the compounds first — then you can see how many moles you've got.

Q7   12.3 g of hydrated $MgSO_4$ crystals are heated strongly.
The crystals turn into a powder with a mass of 6g.

a)   What do chemists call the water that came off from the crystals?

b)   What is the formula for hydrated magnesium sulphate (i.e. including the water in the crystals)?

Q8   The formula for hydrated sodium tetraborate crystals is $Na_2B_4O_7.10H_2O$.

a)   What is the molar mass of hydrated sodium tetraborate?

b)   If 1.91 g of the crystals is heated to drive off all the water, how much will the anhydrous
crystals weigh?

Titration

Q1   Draw a labelled diagram to show the equipment required to carry out a simple titration.

Q2   What colour is phenolphthalein in alkaline solution?

Q3   Write out this paragraph about titrations and fill in the
gaps using the correct word in brackets each time.

Titrations allow you to find out exactly how much (**acid / alkali**) is needed to neutralise a
quantity of alkali, or how much (**acid / alkali**) is needed to neutralise a quantity of acid.
One way to do a titration is to put the alkali in a flask along with some indicator,
e.g. (**phenolphthalein / sodium chloride**). The (**acid / alkali**) is then added, a bit at a time,
and the flask regularly swirled to make sure the acid and alkali (**stay apart / mix together**).
The indicator (**changes colour / explodes**) when all the alkali has been neutralised. It's best
to repeat this process a few times, making sure you get (**the same / different**) values for the
amount of acid needed each time.

Q4   Answer the following questions on concentration of solutions:
- **a)**   What is the concentration of a solution with 1 mole of potassium iodide in 2 dm^3 of solution?
- **b)**   What is the concentration of a solution with 0.5 moles of NH_4Cl in 1500 cm^3 of solution?
- **c)**   What is the concentration of a solution with 0.2 moles of $CuSO_4$ in 750 cm^3 of solution?
- **d)**   How many moles of H_2SO_4 are there in 250 cm^3 of 0.1 mol/dm^3 solution?
- **e)**   How many moles of NaOH are there in 25 cm^3 of 0.2 mol/dm^3 solution?

Q5   A solution of hydrochloric acid is titrated against 25 cm^3 of 0.2 mol/dm^3
aqueous sodium hydroxide, using phenolphthalein as an indicator.
The results of three titrations are as follows: 40.3 cm^3, 40.2 cm^3, 40.2 cm^3.
- **a)**   Write out a balanced equation for the reaction between sodium hydroxide and hydrochloric acid.
- **b)**   What is the reacting ratio of sodium hydroxide to hydrochloric acid?
- **c)**   How many moles of sodium hydroxide reacted in this titration?
- **d)**   What's the concentration of the hydrochloric acid in mol/dm^3?

Q6   Sulphuric acid reacts with potassium hydroxide to produce potassium
sulphate. The balanced equation is $H_2SO_4 + 2KOH \rightarrow K_2SO_4 + 2H_2O$
- **a)**   The results of a titration of sulphuric acid of an unknown concentration with 50 cm^3 of
0.2 mol/dm^3 potassium hydroxide are as follows: 49.6 cm^3, 50.1 cm^3, 49.8 cm^3.
Calculate the concentration of the acid.
- **b)**   Why can't you just evaporate the water off the neutralised solution in the flask to get a
pure sample of potassium sulphate? (Hint: what else is in the flask?)

Top Tips... Titration needs a bit of practice to get it right. Titration questions need practice too.
With titrations, it's important to work out the reacting ratio — how many moles of acid react with how
many moles of alkali. But you can work this out from the balanced equation, so it's not too bad really.

Instrumental Methods

Q1 There are various ways to determine when the neutralisation point of a reaction has been reached. Explain how the following could be used to determine when a solution has been neutralised.

   a)   pH

   b)   Heat change

   c)   Conductivity

Q2 *Electronic instruments are used instead of bench lab tests to analyse samples in police forensic work.*

   Give two more examples of electronic instruments being used for chemical analysis.

Note: some instrumental methods may be less useful than others.

Q3 Give three advantages of using instrumental methods for chemical analysis.

Q4 There have been huge advances in electronics and computing over the last 10-20 years. What impact has this had on the development of instrumental methods for chemical analysis?

Q5 Fill in the gaps in the paragraphs about spectroscopes using some of the words on the left.

litmus paper test

spectrum

compound

flame test

element

reflected

absorbed

identification

An **atomic emission spectroscope** works a bit like a lab test (a _____), and is used for identifying elements. A sample is injected into a very hot flame, and the whole _____ of light is analysed. Each _____ present in the sample produces a unique spectrum.

Using **infra-red spectroscopy**, the _____ under investigation is placed in the path of infra-red radiation and the amount of each frequency that's _____ is plotted. The pattern of absorbance is unique for different compounds. This 'fingerprint' allows _____ of individual compounds.

Q6 *A computer database can hold details of a vast number of chemical compounds and their spectrograph results.*

   Explain how computer database programs could be used to speed up the process of chemical analysis.

Top Tips... This is more like it — just sit back and let the fancy machines do all the work. Unfortunately, no machine can learn all this stuff for you. You really need to know the difference between atomic emission and infra-red spectroscopy. Don't blame me — I didn't make the rules.

Section Four — Preparing and Analysing

Water

These questions are about water — sea water, fresh water and tap water.

Q1   What other name is given to sea water?

Q2   Copy this out and fill in the blanks.

Sea water is a _____ of many different _____.
The main one is _____.

Q3   Describe what a salt pan is and how it's used.

Q4   Carbon dioxide dissolves in water. Does it produce an
acidic solution, an alkaline solution or a neutral solution?

Q5   Choose the balanced symbol equation
from the list which represents the
reaction of carbon dioxide with water.

$$C_2 + H_2O \rightarrow H_2CO_3$$

$$CO_2 + H_2O \rightarrow H_2CO_3$$

$$CO_2 + 2H_2O \rightarrow H_2CO_3$$

$$CO_2 + H_2O \rightarrow 3H_2CO_3$$

Q6   Name four things which have to be removed from
fresh water before it's safe to be supplied to homes.

Q7   Older water pipes are made from iron.

   a)   What compound do these old pipes sometimes release into drinking water?

   b)   What problem does this cause when cooking vegetables?

   c)   What does this compound do to tea?

   d)   What does this compound do to laundry?

Q8   Why is chlorine added during treatment of the domestic water supply?

Q9   What chemical is used to remove excess chlorine?

Q10   Aluminium sulphate is used in the water treatment process.

   a)   What impurity is removed by aluminium sulphate?

   b)   Which ion is responsible for removing the impurity — Al^{3+} or SO_4^{2-}?

   c)   After the aluminium sulphate is added, what has to be done next?

Q11   Two types of slurry are used in the water purification process.

   a)   Name them.

   b)   Say what impurities or chemicals each one removes.

   c)   There's a balanced ionic equation for the action of one of the kinds of slurry. Write it out.

Colloids

Q1   Which of the following are colloids?

watered-down clay (slip)

brine

basic salad dressing (oil and vinegar)

mayonnaise

styling mousse

matt paint

Q2   Write down a definition of a colloid.

Q3   What is the disperse phase of a colloid?

Q4   What is the continuous phase of a colloid?

Q5   Give two reasons why colloids don't tend to separate out.

Q6   If a colloid does separate out, is it still a colloid?

Q7   Draw out the table below and decide whether each description is of a solid, a liquid or a gas.

	Description	Solid, liquid or gas?
a)	The continuous phase of a sol	
b)	The disperse phase of a foam	
c)	The disperse phase of an emulsion	
d)	The continuous phase of an emulsion	
e)	The disperse phase of a sol	

Q8   Explain why charged particles attract water molecules to them. Draw a diagram to show water molecules around a negatively charged colloid particle.

Q9   Explain why attracting water molecules helps prevent colloid particles from coagulating.

Q10   How do metal ions cause colloids to coagulate? *(hint — think of the charge on the ion)*

Top Tips...

You've got to know your colloids. They're not particularly thrilling, I'm afraid. The fact is that they're on the syllabus, and there's a page of questions here all about them. The bit you'll need to pay most attention to is the bit about charge on colloid particles keeping them apart.

Section Five — Water and Electrochemistry

Hard Water

Q1   Fill in the gaps in the following paragraph about hard water. Use the words in the kettle.

> Hard water _____ easily form a lather with soap. Hard water
> can also form _____ (also known as _____ carbonate) on
> the insides of kettles. A kettle with _____ on the heating
> element takes _____ to boil than a clean kettle. Hard water
> also causes a scum to form on the surface of _____.

scale tea longer calcium scale won't

Q2   Are non-soap detergents affected by hard water?

Q3   Give two health-related benefits of hard water.

Q4   Hard water usually causes problems but it can be advantageous
with some types of pipework. What are the advantages?

BEWARE: HARD WATER

Q5   Which two cations are responsible for hard water?

Q6   *Hardness in water can be permanent or temporary.*

   a)   Which anions are responsible for permanent hardness in water?
   b)   Which anions are responsible for temporary hardness in water?
   c)   How do the anions responsible for permanent hardness get into water?
   d)   What acid is produced when carbon dioxide dissolves in water?
   e)   What metal salt found in rock reacts with this acid to produce temporary hardness?

Q7   Which kind of hardness can be removed by boiling?

Q8   Write a balanced equation to show water hardness being removed by heat.

Q9   Write a balanced ionic equation to show what happens
when sodium carbonate is added to hard water.

Q10   Describe how an ion exchange column works (in nit-picking detail).

Electrochemistry and Electrolysis

Q1   Copy the diagram on the right. Label the electrodes positive (+) and negative (–). Draw arrows to show the movement of ions ($\oplus$ ▲ , ▲ $\ominus$).

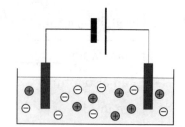

Q2   Molten zinc chloride conducts electricity.

   a)   Write down the ionic equation for the reaction at the cathode.

   b)   Write down the ionic equation for the reaction at the anode.

Q3   Write down the equation relating charge, current and time.

Q4   Answer the following questions about charge, current and time.

   a)   A current of 4 amps flows through a circuit for 8 seconds. How much charge has gone through the circuit?

   b)   A current of 4 amps flows through a circuit for 15 minutes. How much charge is that?

   c)   The current flowing through a circuit with a switch is 3 amps. If 2700 coulombs of charge passed through the circuit while the switch was closed, for how many minutes was the switch closed?

Q5   How many coulombs are there in one faraday?

Q6   How many electrons are there in one faraday?

Q7   How many moles of electrons are needed for each of the following?

   a)   Reducing one mole of sodium ions to sodium.

   b)   Reducing one mole of calcium ions to calcium.

   c)   Reducing one mole of zinc ions to zinc.

   d)   Reducing one mole of iron (III) ions to iron.

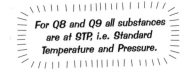

For Q8 and Q9 all substances are at STP, i.e. Standard Temperature and Pressure.

Q8   Answer the following electrolysis questions:

   a)   How many moles of chlorine are made in the electrolysis of molten sodium chloride, if 0.5 faradays of charge has passed through the circuit?

   b)   How many moles of aluminium are made in the electrolysis of molten aluminium oxide, if 9600 coulombs of charge has passed through the circuit?

   c)   How many moles of zinc are made in the electrolysis of zinc chloride, if a charge of 6 amps flows for 20 minutes?

Q9   Answer the following slightly trickier electrolysis questions:

   a)   If 2 amps flows through the electrolysis of copper (II) chloride for 30 minutes, find the mass of copper and the volume of chlorine liberated.

   b)   If 6 amps flows through the electrolysis of iron (III) bromide for 15 minutes, find the mass of iron and the volume of bromine liberated.

   c)   Molten magnesium iodide is electrolysed for 20 minutes. The mass of magnesium liberated is 6 g. What is the current used?

Section Five — Water and Electrochemistry

Electrochemical Cells

Q1 Sketch out this diagram of an electrochemical cell and label the following on it: cathode, anode, electrolyte, more reactive metal, less reactive metal.

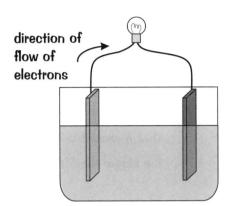

direction of
flow of
electrons

Q2 The electrodes of an electrochemical cell are made from two different metals.

  a) Will it work if the electrodes are made from the same metal? Give a reason for your answer.

  b) What do chemists call the kind of reaction where a more reactive metal reacts with a solution of a salt of a less reactive metal?

Q3 A strip of magnesium and a strip of copper are dipped into a copper sulphate solution, and connected by a wire.

  a) Which metal gives up electrons, and forms metal ions?

  b) Which metal is the anode, and which is the cathode?

I just can't get you out of my head

Boy, your lovin' is all I think about.

Q4 At the cathode of an electrochemical cell, metal ions take up electrons and turn into metal atoms.

  a) Where do these metal ions come from?

  b) Where do the electrons come from?

Q5 Fill in the gaps in the following sentences.

  a) Oxidation is .... of electrons.

  b) Reduction is .... of electrons.

  c) Oxidation happens at the .... electrode (the ....).

  d) Reduction happens at the .... electrode (the ....).

Q6 A strip of zinc and a strip of iron are dipped into an iron chloride solution, and connected by a wire.

  a) Write down the half-equation for what happens at the anode.

  b) Write down the half-equation for what happens at the cathode.

  c) How do electrons get from the anode to the cathode?

Electrochemical Cells

Q7   Write out the following paragraph, choosing one of the words in brackets each time.

> The bigger the difference between the reactivity of the metal of the
> (*anode* / *cathode*) and the metal of the (*anode* / *cathode*), the
> (*more* / *less*) electrons move from the anode to the cathode.
> That means that the (*smaller* / *bigger*) the difference in reactivity,
> the bigger the (*current* / *voltage*) of the cell.

Q8   Explain how the reduction and oxidation reactions in an
electrochemical cell drive the current through the circuit.

Q9   How does a fuel cell make electricity?

Q10   Hydrogen fuel cells use hydrogen and oxygen.

   a)   Give the half-equation at the anode.

   b)   Give the half-equation at the cathode

   c)   Where do the cations in the cathode half-
equation come from?

   d)   Give an example of a use for hydrogen fuel cells.

Q11   Use the table to work out the voltage
produced by the following cells.

   a)   A cell with magnesium and tin(II) electrodes.

   b)   A cell with iron(II) and copper electrodes.

   c)   A cell with copper and silver electrodes.

   d)   A cell with zinc and silver electrodes.

   e)   A cell with aluminium and cadmium electrodes.

   f)   A cell with nickel and cadmium electrodes.

   g)   A cell with chromium and lead electrodes.

*Standard electrode potentials
of 11 elements*

$Mg^{2+}_{(aq)} + 2e^-$	$\rightleftharpoons$	$Mg_{(s)}$	-2.38
$Al^{3+}_{(aq)} + 3e^-$	$\rightleftharpoons$	$Al_{(s)}$	-1.66
$Zn^{2+}_{(aq)} + 2e^-$	$\rightleftharpoons$	$Zn_{(s)}$	-0.76
$Fe^{2+}_{(aq)} + 2e^-$	$\rightleftharpoons$	$Fe_{(s)}$	-0.44
$Cr^{3+}_{(aq)} + e^-$	$\rightleftharpoons$	$Cr^{2+}_{(aq)}$	-0.41
$Cd^{2+}_{(aq)} + 2e^-$	$\rightleftharpoons$	$Cd_{(s)}$	-0.40
$Ni^{2+}_{(aq)} + 2e^-$	$\rightleftharpoons$	$Ni_{(s)}$	-0.25
$Sn^{2+}_{(aq)} + 2e^-$	$\rightleftharpoons$	$Sn_{(s)}$	-0.14
$Pb^{2+}_{(aq)} + 2e^-$	$\rightleftharpoons$	$Pb_{(s)}$	-0.13
$Cu^{2+}_{(aq)} + 2e^-$	$\rightleftharpoons$	$Cu_{(s)}$	0.34
$Ag^+_{(aq)} + e^-$	$\rightleftharpoons$	$Ag_{(s)}$	0.80

Top Tips...

All the stuff on electrochemical cells boils down to <u>learning</u> what happens at the anode and at the cathode.
And that means that you first need to learn the difference between the anode and the cathode, obviously.

Aluminium and Titanium

Aluminium and titanium are both really useful metals.

Q1   Is aluminium reactive or unreactive? Where does it come in the reactivity series?

Q2   Aluminium is resistant to corrosion. Why is this?

Q3   Write out the paragraph, using the correct word from the pair in brackets each time.

The natural oxide layer is first removed using (**sodium chloride / sodium hydroxide**) solution. The aluminium is then made the (**anode / cathode**) of an electrolysis cell, with (**hydrochloric / sulphuric**) acid as the electrolyte. Oxygen forms on the surface of the aluminium, and reacts to form (**aluminium oxide / aluminium carbonate**). This anodising process makes the aluminium (**resistant / susceptible**) to corrosion.

Q4   Anodising aluminium involves electrolysis.

    a)   What substance is electrolysed?

    b)   What is the reaction at the anode?

    c)   What happens to the aluminium?

Q5   Why is aluminium usually alloyed?

Q6   Give three uses of aluminium.

Q7   What physical properties make titanium a very useful metal?

Q8   Give examples of three uses of titanium.

Q9   What is the main ore of titanium?

Q10   Titanium is low in the reactivity series, and could be extracted from its ore by reduction by carbon. Why isn't carbon used to extract titanium?

Q11   Titanium ore is converted into a titanium salt before being reduced. Choose the correct formula for the salt from the options on the right.
TCl_4 $TiCl_4$ $TiCl_2$ TiO_4

Q12   The titanium salt is reduced to titanium metal.

    a)   What substances are used to reduce the salt to titanium metal?

    b)   What process is used to obtain the reducing agents?

    c)   What other products are formed in the reduction of titanium?

    d)   How is contamination by nitrogen or oxygen prevented in the reaction between the titanium salt and the reducing agent?

    e)   Explain why these conditions are chosen.

Q13   Use the details of the extraction process to explain why titanium is so expensive.

Iron, Steel and Alloys

Q1 What are the uses of pure iron? Why are these uses limited?

Q2 What is steel? Write out the correct definition.

An alloy of iron containing between 5% and 15% carbon.

An alloy of iron containing between 0.05% and 1.5% carbon.

An alloy of iron containing between 50% and 99% carbon.

Q3 Write out this paragraph, filling in the gaps with the words in the box.

| carbon | calcium oxide | scrap iron | oxides | slag | alloys | oxygen | sulphur dioxide |

In the first stage of producing steel, impure molten iron from the blast furnace is mixed with _____ and as it is heated, _____ is blasted through. This converts all the non-metal impurities to _____. Carbon dioxide and _____ come off as gases. Calcium carbonate is also added — this decomposes to form _____ (CaO) and carbon dioxide. Calcium oxide reacts with any non-metal oxides to form '_____'. _____ and metals are then added to give the required _____.

Q4 Give the balanced equation for the main reaction that forms slag.

Q5 Which reaction in the manufacture of iron is an acid / base reaction?

Moral Laxity + Insufficient Skin Coverage $\xrightarrow[\text{Catalyst}]{\text{Alcohol}}$ ....

[1 mark]

Q6 Why are metals alloyed?

Q7 Copy and complete the table:

	Carbon content	Properties	Uses
Cast Iron		Hard but brittle	Castings of drains, stoves, etc.
High carbon steel		Very hard	
Mild Steel		Shaped easily by pressing	
	Contain chromium and/or nickel	Corrosion-resistant and strong	Food vessels, marine and chemical use
Titanium steel	Contains titanium		Armour plating, for example
Manganese steels	Contains manganese		Grinding machinery, caterpillar tracks

Q8 What are the alloy components of brass?

Q9 What are the components of soft solder?

Q10 What is solder used for? Which physical property of solder makes it suitable for this use?

Protecting Iron and Steel

Q1   Under what conditions will iron or steel oxidise to form rust?

Q2   Explain how the following methods help prevent rusting:

   a)   painting

   b)   oiling

   c)   galvanising

   d)   sacrificial protection

   e)   alloying

Q3   Which of the following is a definition of electroplating?

Using electrolysis to coat a non-metal with a layer of a metal.	Using electrolysis to coat one metal with a layer of another.	Using electrolysis to coat a metal with a layer of a non-metal.	Using special crockery that keeps your dinner nice and warm.

Q4   Electroplating is used to coat a lump of iron with a thin layer of copper.
Copy the diagram and label each metal, the moving ions and the electrolyte.

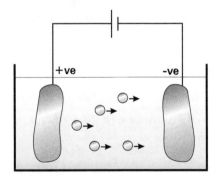

Q5   Write an explanation of the movement of the electrons in the above example of electroplating.

Q6   Explain how it is that the concentration of copper in the solution remains constant.

Q7   *Steel can be electroplated with silver.*

   a)   Which electrode must the piece of steel be? Explain why.

   b)   What is the other electrode made from?

   c)   What metal ions must the electrolyte solution contain?

Sulphuric Acid

Q1   What are the raw materials in the manufacture of sulphuric acid?

Q2   Answer the following questions about the Contact Process.

  a)   How is the sulphur dioxide made?

  b)   Write a balanced equation for the reaction between
            sulphur dioxide and oxygen.

  c)   What catalyst is used most often in this reaction?

  d)   What are the physical conditions under which the
            reaction is carried out?

  e)   What is the next stage in the process? Write a
            balanced equation to show what happens.

  f)   Why is sulphur trioxide not dissolved in water?

  g)   What is the final step in making sulphuric acid?

*Simple dehydrating agent
no.1: the towel.*

Q3   What is oleum?

Q4   Answer these questions about the Contact Process.

  a)   Is the reaction between sulphur dioxide and oxygen exothermic or endothermic?

  b)   How many moles of reactant react to produce two moles of product?

  c)   State Le Chatelier's Principle.

  d)   What pressure conditions favour a high yield of product?

  e)   What temperature conditions favour a high rate of reaction?

  f)   Why are the actual industrial conditions of the Contact Process a compromise?

Q5   Which three of the following is sulphuric acid used for?

  making   making   car batteries   making   making
  fertilisers   paint   detergents   sausages

Q6   What is a dehydrating agent?

Q7   Write down a balanced equation for the
           reaction between sulphuric acid and glucose.

Top Tips...

There's a fair amount to learn about sulphuric acid. Make sure you know all the steps in the
manufacturing process. You also have to be able to explain just why the particular <u>temperature and
pressure</u> conditions are chosen. The important thing is that it's a <u>compromise</u>.

Section Six — Industrial and Organic Chemistry

Homologous Series and Isomers

Q1   What is a homologous series?

Q2   Three chemicals have the same general formula, C_nH_{2n}.

   a)   Are they part of a homologous series?

   b)   If so, give the name of that homologous series.

Q3   What is the name for the part of a molecule that is responsible for the similarities in chemical properties between the members of a homologous series?

Q4   What is the functional group of carboxylic acids?

Q5   Pentane is C_5H_{12}. Look at these structural diagrams.

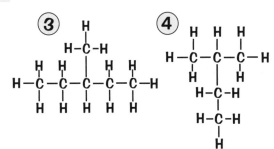

   a)   Which of these are pentane molecules?

   b)   What term is given to molecules with the same formula but different molecular structure?

   c)   Which pentane do you think will have the highest boiling point? Explain your answer.

Q6   Copy and complete the following sentence:

The strength of intermolecular forces .... as the length of the carbon chain .... and .... as the amount of chain branching ....

Q7   This is 2-methylpropane.

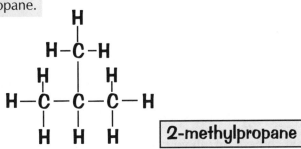

2-methylpropane

   a)   Draw a diagram to show what you think the structure of 3-ethylpentane would be.

   b)   Draw a diagram to show what you think the structure of 2,3-methylhexane would be.

Alcohols

Q1   What is the functional group in the alcohols?

Q2   Draw the structural formula of ethanol.

Q3   Write out balanced equations for the combustion of the following alcohols.

    a)   methanol

    b)   ethanol

    c)   propanol

Essential wine ingredient no. 23: foot odour.

Q4   What is the product of the reaction between an alcohol and a carboxylic acid called?

Q5   Write out a balanced equation for the reaction between propanol and sodium.

Q6   What other reaction of sodium is this similar to?

Q7   Give an example of a use of ethanol.

Q8   Copy and complete the following table about typical amounts of alcohol in drinks:

Drink	Beer	Wine	Spirits
% Alcohol by volume			

Q9   *Methylated spirit is mostly ethanol.*

    a)   What other alcohol does it contain?

    b)   Why is this alcohol added?

    c)   Why does methylated spirit also contain a purple dye?

Alcohol can be important as a social lubricant.

Q10   *Cholesterol is a steroid hormone produced by the body.*

    a)   What does the name cholesterol tell you about the molecular structure? What functional group must it contain?

    b)   What disease has been associated with excessive amounts of cholesterol?

Ethanol

Q1 *Ethanol has traditionally been made by the fermentation of carbohydrates.*

   a)   Give some examples of sources of carbohydrates traditionally fermented to make ethanol.

   b)   Write a balanced equation for the fermentation of glucose.

   c)   What is the catalyst for the fermentation of carbohydrate?

   d)   At what temperature is the reaction rate highest?

   e)   Why is air prevented from entering the vessel where fermentation takes place?

Q2 *Ethanol can also be made industrially.*

   a)   What two chemicals react together to make ethanol?

   b)   Write a balanced equation to show the reaction.

   c)   What are the industrial conditions under which the reaction takes place?

Q3 Copy and complete the table below.

	Fermentation	Hydration of ethene
Economic advantages	1.	1.
	2.	2.
		3.
Is it a finite resource?		
Is it a batch process?		

Q4 Which are more efficient for large-scale production — batch processes or continuous processes?

Mmmm veggie-beer.
Drink it smooth, or crunchy.

Q5 *Ethanol can be dehydrated by passing it over a heated catalyst.*

   a)   What are the products of the dehydration of ethanol?

   b)   What is the catalyst used?

Carboxylic Acids

Q1   What is the functional group of the homologous series of carboxylic acids?

Q2   Which of the following shows the structural formula of this functional group?

$$-C\overset{OH}{\underset{OH}{\diagup}} \qquad -C\overset{O}{\underset{OH}{\diagdown}} \qquad -C\overset{O}{\underset{OH}{\diagdown}} \qquad -C\overset{O}{\underset{OH}{\diagdown}}$$

Q3   Are carboxylic acids weak or strong acids?

Q4   Draw the structural formula of methanoic acid.

Q5   Copy and complete the following table.

Carboxylic acid reacting with...	Result
	forms salts and hydrogen
carbonates	
hydrogencarbonates	forms salts, carbon dioxide and water
alkalis	
	turns red

Q6   Fill in the gaps in this paragraph, using the correct word from each pair in brackets.

Ethanoic acid is the acid in (**mustard** / **vinegar**). If wine or beer is left open to the air, the ethanol is (**oxidised** / **distilled**) to ethanoic acid. Ethanoic acid is also used in the manufacture of a synthetic fibre called (**rayon** / **crayon**). Oranges and lemons contain (**methanoic acid** / **citric acid**). An example of a man-made carboxylic acid is (**aspirin** / **rayon**).

Q7   Write a word equation to show the reaction when wine is left out in an open bottle.

Q8   What is ascorbic acid also known as?

Q9   Where is ascorbic acid found?

Section Six — Industrial and Organic Chemistry

Esters

Q1   Write down a general word equation for the formation of esters.

Q2   What is used as a catalyst in the lab for the reaction to make esters?

Q3   Draw out the following example of esterification. On your version, highlight the parts of the reactants that react to form water.

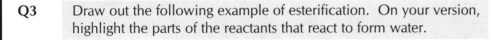

Q4   What ester is made in each of the following reactions?

    a)   Methanol and propanoic acid

    b)   Ethanol and methanoic acid

    c)   Butanol and ethanoic acid

    d)   Propanol and butanoic acid

Q5   Write down a balanced equation for the reaction between methanol and ethanoic acid.

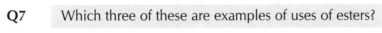

Q6   What property of esters makes them useful?

Q7   Which three of these are examples of uses of esters?

    shoe   ointments   fruit

    soles   perfumes   paper   flavourings

Q8   Draw the structures of the following esters.

    a)   ethyl ethanoate

    b)   propyl methanoate

    c)   methyl ethanoate

Top Tips...

Fantastic! A whole page on esters — although not to be confused with TV's favourite set of teeth, Esther Rantzen. Esterification involves some pretty ugly formula diagrams, but I have complete faith that you'll be able to produce them blindfolded soon. If necessary, that is.

Free Radicals

Q1 *Free radicals are made when covalent bonds break.*

   a) How many electrons are there in a single covalent bond?

   b) What happens when a covalent bond breaks unevenly?

   c) What happens when a covalent bond breaks evenly?

Q2 What is a free radical?

Q3 How many free electrons are there in a free radical?

Q4 What's special about the behaviour of free radicals?

Q5 What are chlorofluorocarbons? Write out the correct definition: "Chlorofluorocarbons are...

   ...elements similar to   ...organic molecules containing   ...cakes containing flour
   fluorine and chlorine   fluorine and chlorine   and orange juice

Q6 Give two uses for chlorofluorocarbons.

Q7 *Dichlorodifluoromethane (Cl_2F_2C) can break up to form free radicals.*

   a) What is the catalyst for this reaction?

   b) Where in the atmosphere does this reaction occur, and why?

   c) Write a balanced equation to show dichlorodifluoromethane splitting into two free radicals.

Q8 What does the ozone layer do?

Q9 What does damage to the ozone layer allow to happen?

Q10 *Chlorine free radicals act on ozone high in the atmosphere.*

   a) Write an equation to show the action of a chlorine free radical on ozone.

   b) What happens to the chlorine oxide produced by this reaction?

   c) One chlorine free radical can break up a large number of ozone molecules. Why is this?

Q11 Name three health risks that are increased by damage to the ozone layer?

Q12 *Since the 1990s, butane has been used as a propellant in aerosols in Europe.*

   a) Why is this?

   b) Have all the countries of the world started using butane (or another alternative to CFCs) as an aerosol propellant?

   c) Why has European law introduced restrictions on how refrigerators are disposed of?

Top Tips...

You may well have already heard of the hole in the ozone layer. That's no excuse to avoid doing these questions, mind. Free radicals (with the dot) are almost certainly a Shiny New Thing, so keep your brain in gear. If you can't figure out the answers, then do a spot more learning.

Section Six — Industrial and Organic Chemistry

Carbohydrates

Q1   *There are three main nutrients in food.*

a) What are these three main nutrients?

b) Which of these types of nutrient are glucose, sucrose and starch?

Q2   *All carbohydrates are made up of the same three elements.*

a) Name the three elements which make up carbohydrates.

b) Draw the structural formula for glucose.

c) Name three carbohydrates other than glucose.

Q3   *Monosaccharides and disaccharides are both types of sugar.*

a) Copy and complete these sentences:

Glucose is a _____. Sucrose is a _____.

b) Draw the structural formula for sucrose.

Q4   Answer these questions on polysaccharides.

a) What is a polysaccharide?

b) What do you call the type of reaction which creates polysaccharides?

c) What's the by-product of this reaction?

d) Give two examples of polysaccharides.

e) What's the monomer of each of these polysaccharides?

Q5   Look at these diagrams. Name carbohydrate A and carbohydrate B.

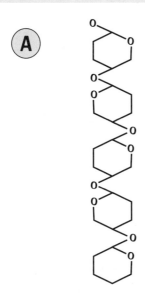

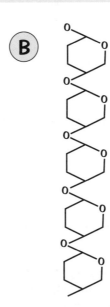

Proteins and Fats

Q1   Pick out the amino acid from the box below.

Q2   Glycine is the simplest amino acid.
Draw its structural formula.

Q3   What kind of nutrient is formed from polymers of amino acids?

Q4   What kind of reaction joins amino acids into long chains?

Q5   Draw the structures of the products formed when two amino acids join together.

Q6   What is formed when glycerol and carboxylic acids combine?

Q7   Draw the structural formula of a triglyceride.

Q8   By what type of reaction are each of the following broken down into their constituent parts?
   a) starch
   b) polypeptides
   c) triglycerides

Top Tips...

There are a few important similarities between polypeptides, polysaccharides and triglycerides. Firstly, they're all pretty dull. Secondly, as they're produced, water molecules are formed. Thirdly, they can all be broken down by water (or in fancy chemistry lingo 'by hydrolysis'). Finally, they're all pretty dull.

Diet

Q1 Name three groups of people who need more food than an 'average adult'.

Q2 Write a sentence to say why each of the following is needed as part of a balanced diet.

   a) protein
   b) fat
   c) carbohydrate
   d) fibre

Q3 Write down a food you could eat to get each of the nutrients in Q2.

Q4 Match each vitamin and mineral to the reason we need it. You can use reasons more than once.

   a) vitamin A
   b) vitamin C (three reasons)
   c) vitamin D
   d) calcium
   e) iron

For making haemoglobin.   For making pigment in the eye.

Keeps the skin strong and supple.   Prevents scurvy.

Strengthens bones and teeth.   Destroys harmful free radicals.

Q5 Why does a vegetarian need to take extra care to make sure that his or her diet is balanced?

Q6 *Fats can be divided into two categories, depending on their molecular structure.*

What are the two categories?

Q7 Pick the correct words out of the brackets to make each sentence true.

   a) Unsaturated fats come mainly from [**plants** / **animals**].
   b) Saturated fats come mainly from [**plants** / **animals**].
   c) Unsaturated fats [**have** / **do not have**] C=C double bonds in their carbon chains.
   d) Unsaturated fats are [**healthier** / **less healthy**] than saturated fats.
   e) Eating excessive [**unsaturated** / **saturated**] fat increases the risk of heart disease.

Q8 *Margarine is made from vegetable oils.*

What is done to oils to turn them into hard, spreadable fats?

Q9 Do human beings get any energy from cellulose?

Diet

Q10 *Vitamin C is beneficial to health.*

   a) What foods naturally contain a lot of vitamin C?

   b) What happens to the vitamin C content of food when it's cooked?

   c) What happens to the vitamin C content of food when it's stored for too long?

Q11 *Raising agents make bread and cakes rise when cooked. Baking powder used in cakes contains sodium hydrogencarbonate (which is a base) and potassium tartrate (which is an acid).*

   a) What gas is released when baking powder becomes wet?

   b) What happens to this gas when the temperature rises (i.e. when the cake is in the oven)?

   c) What raising agent is used in bread?

   d) How does this raising agent produce bubbles of gas?

Q12 Complete the sentences below with words from the box.

| good | purple penguins | taste | vinegar | fattening | preservatives |
| blood | food | chemicals | salt | colourings | sweetener |

   a) Additives are _____ added to _____.

   b) Some additives are totally harmless, and some are even _____ for you.
However, some additives are known to be bad for you. For example, too much _____
is thought to cause high _____ pressure.

   c) Sometimes additives are used as flavourings, to improve _____.

   d) _____ are often added to make food last longer.

   e) Nutrasweet is an example of a _____ which is added to make food taste sweet
without being _____.

   f) _____ are sometimes used to make food look more appetising.

Q13 *"None of the chemicals used as food additives occur naturally."* True or false?

Top Tips...

My mum said that spinach would put some colour in my cheeks — but she didn't say what colour, and I didn't want to take the chance of getting green cheeks. But anyway... I reckon the trickiest part of this topic is remembering which vitamins and minerals are needed for what. Apart from that it's not so bad.

<u>Drugs</u>

Q1   Complete the definition of drugs using words from the box below.

gas   reduce   externally   alter   sloppily   chemistry   monkey

Drugs are substances that .... your body ....

Q2   Answer these questions about analgesics:

    a) What is an analgesic?

    b) Name three commonly used analgesics.

Q3   In the old days, bark from a type of willow tree was used as a painkiller.

    a) What chemical in the willow bark was responsible for the painkilling effect?

    b) This drug had a rather unfortunate side effect — what was it?

Q4   Draw the structural formula of aspirin.

Q5   Why is aspirin used to help prevent heart attacks and strokes?

Q6   *Aspirin molecules are not very soluble.*

    a) How is a soluble form of aspirin produced?

    b) In what way is this soluble aspirin better than normal aspirin?

Q7   A drugs company 'Willit Kilewe' is testing a new product. Put these stages in the right order:

Tested on cells growing in tissue culture.	Clinical trials with tens of thousands of patients.	Tested on small group of volunteers.
Clinical trials with several hundred patients.	Tested on laboratory animals.	

Interesting(ish) fact:
Placebos seem to be more 'effective' when they're big and brightly coloured.

Q8   What are placebos? How are they used in testing drugs?

Dealing with Information

Q1 A singer is being recorded. The singer sings into a microphone. The output signal, in volts, from the microphone over 0.1 seconds is shown below.

a) Is this an analogue or a digital signal?

b) What were the minimum and maximum values of the signal?

c) What values can the signal have between these minimum and maximum limits?

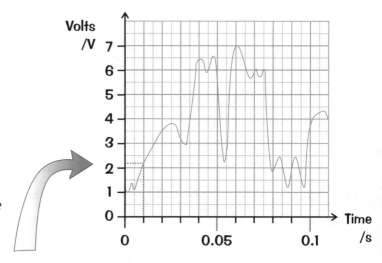

A recording device is used to store the signal in digital form. It does this by sampling the signal every 0.01 s, reading it to the nearest volt.
For example, the value of the signal at 0.01 s is 2.3 V, so the device reads this as 2 V. The device stores these numbers in binary form (zeros and ones).

Time (S)	Reading to nearest V	Binary Number
0.00		
0.01	2	010
0.02		
0.03		
0.04		
0.05		
0.06		
0.07		
0.08		
0.09		
0.10		

Decimal	Binary
0	000
1	001
2	010
3	011
4	100
5	101
6	110
7	111

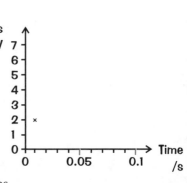

I woke up this morning, Feelin' so blue...

d) Take readings from the graph to help copy and complete the table above. Use the table on the right to help you write the voltage in binary form.

e) How many 0s and 1s are stored in total for this 0.1 second of singing?

The stored digital information is then converted back (reconstructed) to an analogue signal and sent to a loudspeaker.

f) Copy and complete the graph opposite to show the reconstructed analogue signal. One point has been plotted for you.

g) Compare your reconstructed signal with the original. Comment on any differences. Would it sound the same?

h) Would the reconstructed signal be a better copy of the original if

   i) the sampling was every 0.001 s?

   ii) the values were read to the nearest ½ volt?

i) If each of these changes were made (sampling every 0.001 s and values read to the nearest ½ volt), what would be the effect on the number of 0s and 1s stored for each second of sampling?

Dealing with Information

Q2 The inside of a compact disc (CD) player is shown below. The CD contains information that is read by the player.

a) What would you see if you looked at the playing surface of a CD under a microscope?

b) Do CDs store information in analogue or digital form?

c) How many different states have to be encoded on the CD in order to store this information?

d) Name the part labelled X.

e) Name the part labelled Y.

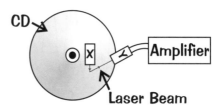

Q3 A vinyl LP is shown below. It contains information that can be read by a record player.

a) What would you see if you looked at the playing surface of a vinyl record under a microscope?

b) Is the information on a vinyl record stored in analogue or digital form?

c) How does the record player read the information?

d) How might a scratch on a record affect the listening experience?

Q4 Copy and complete the following paragraph using the words below.

| analogue | digital | noise | attenuation | amplified |
| regenerator | | hiss | signal | remove |

_____ is the process whereby a signal gets weaker the further it travels. The signal can be _____ by repeater stations, but they often introduce _____ and distortion. Random noise sounds like a _____. However, a _____ can be used to restore a digital signal's wave shape, so that it's exactly the same as the original. In _____ signals, noise is very hard to _____ because systems can't easily distinguish the noise from the original signal. _____ signals, on the other hand, don't suffer from noise in the same way. As long as a zero won't be mistaken for a one, or vice versa, the _____ will be read correctly.

Top Tips...

Vinyl LP's aren't so popular nowadays, mostly because CD's sound tons better and don't break so easily. Many club DJ's still play vinyl though. It's easier to mix tracks and 'scratch', if you're into old skool hip hop etc. Ignore that — just remember the advantages and disadvantages of digital and analogue sound.

Radio Waves

Q1 Radio signals are transmitted by 'modulating' a carrier wave.

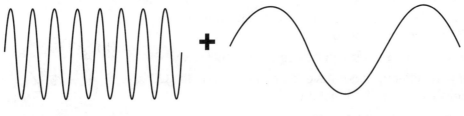

Carrier Wave   **Signal wave**

a) Draw the carrier wave after amplitude modulation (AM) by the signal wave.

b) Give the main characteristic of a carrier wave.

c) Which has the highest frequency carrier wave, an AM or an FM signal?

d) Give one advantage of sending information as AM signals
and one advantage of sending information as FM signals.

Q2 Communication systems are often very complex. Copy out the parts of the system below,
and for each part write down the descriptions, functions and devices that best match it.
Each part of the system might have more than one description, function or device.

PART OF SYSTEM:

| Modulator |
| Demodulator |
| Storage System |
| Transmitter |
| Receiver |
| Amplifier |
| Encoder |
| Decoder |
| Transducer |

DESCRIPTIONS, FUNCTIONS AND DEVICES:

Aerial

Sends out a signal

Accepts a signal

Increases the amplitude of a signal

Removes a carrier wave from an **AM** or **FM** signal

Converts information into a form suitable for transmission

Extracts information from a received signal

Increases the strength of an attenuated signal

Encodes information onto a carrier wave by changing its amplitude

Microphone

DVD

Magnetic tape

Encodes information onto a carrier wave by changing its frequency

Transforms energy from one form to another

Radio Waves

Q3 An AM radio set receives many radio waves that it 'picks up' with its aerial.
The diagram shows a particular AM radio signal that the user wishes to listen to.

a) What do the radio signals produce in the aerial?

b) A particular radio station can be selected with the tuner. What is actually being tuned into?

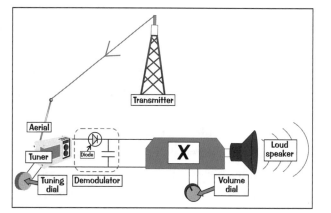

In the demodulator there are two important components — one is a diode.

c) What does a diode do to an alternating current?

d) Draw the signal before and after the diode.

The other component in the demodulator removes the carrier wave to leave the original signal.

e) What is the name of this component?

f) What is the device labelled X?

g) Describe how the signal changes after passing through X.

Q4 Radio waves travel from a transmitting aerial to a receiving aerial in three ways: as ground waves, sky waves and space waves.

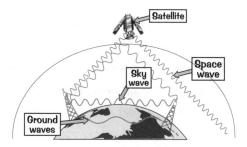

a) Will ground waves travel further over sand dunes or a lake? Explain your answer.

b) What radio bands use ground waves as the main method of transmission? What range of frequencies do these bands cover?

c) What is the name given to the layer of the atmosphere that reflects sky waves?

d) Can a radio wave of frequency 10 MHz reflect off a layer of the atmosphere?

e) Why is the shape of the Earth an important factor when sending and receiving radio waves over long distances?

f) Are FM radio signals good for sending information over long distances?

g) Why are very high frequency carrier waves used for communicating via satellites?

h) Is a spy satellite an active or passive satellite?

Transducers

Q1 The loudspeaker below is connected to an amplifier. The amplifier is
sending a signal to the loudspeaker. The loudspeaker is playing music.

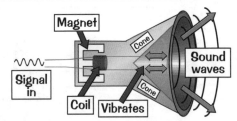

a) Is the amplifier sending a d.c. or an a.c. signal to the loudspeaker?

b) What is created when a current flows in the coil?

c) Why is there a force exerted on the coil?

d) What determines the direction of the force on the coil?

e) Is there a force on the permanent magnet? Does it move? Explain your answers.

f) Why does the cone vibrate?

g) How does the signal determine the frequency of the vibration?

h) What is the overall energy transfer in the loudspeaker?

Q2 A tuning fork is struck and held near to the moving-coil microphone below.

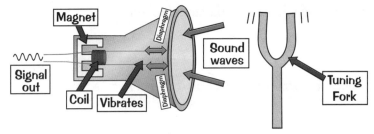

Match the beginnings and endings of the sentences below.
Then put the completed sentences in the correct order.

The signal can pass through an amplifier and	depends on the frequency of the sound wave.
The coil is attached to the diaphragm	either be recorded or sent to a loudspeaker.
The sound wave causes the air particles to vibrate	and this causes the diaphragm to vibrate back and forth.
The direction of the voltage induced	induces a voltage in the coil.
Energy travels from the tuning fork	created by the permanent magnet.
Moving through the magnetic field	to the microphone in the form of a sound wave.
The frequency of the signal produced in the coil	depends on the direction of movement of the coil.
The coil moves through the magnetic field	and therefore the coil also moves back and forth.

Q3 A magnetic tape contains domains (tiny magnetised areas) that are initially pointing in random
directions. A recording head in a tape machine can produce a pattern in these domains.

a) An electrical signal from an amplifier is passed into the coil on the recording head.
What does this produce in the small gap on the recording head?

b) What features of the signal determine the pattern of domains recorded?

c) During playback, how is a signal produced in the playback head?

d) What is passed through the coil of an erase head when it is erasing?

Optical Devices

Q1 Copy and complete the following sentences about lenses, choosing the correct word(s) in brackets.

a) When light travels from air to glass it **(slows down / speeds up)**.

b) If the light hits the glass at an angle to the normal line, it will change **(frequency / direction)**.

c) When light emerges from glass into air it **(slows down / speeds up)**.

d) A converging lens is **(convex / concave)** and **(brings light to a focus / spreads the light out)**.

e) A diverging lens is **(convex / concave)** and **(brings light to a focus / spreads the light out)**.

f) A diverging lens has a **(real / virtual)** focus point.

g) When a converging lens in a slide projector forms an image on a screen the image is **(real / virtual)** and **(upright / inverted)** and **(larger / smaller)** than the object.

h) When a converging lens is used as a magnifying glass the image formed is **(real / virtual)**, **(upright / inverted)** and **(larger / smaller)** than the object.

Q2 Copy the diagram below of part of a converging lens with two partially drawn rays of light. Complete the path of each ray.

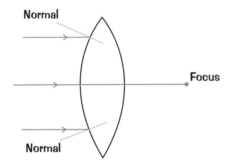

Remember that the light will change direction when it enters and when it leaves the lens. The first normal line has been drawn to help you — but you must draw a normal line whenever the light hits a boundary.

Q3 The ray diagram below shows how a person sees the reflection of an object in a mirror.

a) Why is the image in the mirror said to be a virtual image?

b) If you go to the cinema to watch a movie, is the image on the screen real or virtual? Explain your answer.

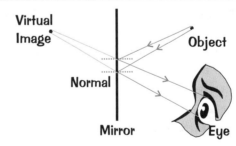

Q4 Light from an object passes through the lens in our eye and is focused to form an image.

a) What type of lens is found in the eye?

b) If the eye is working properly, where will a sharp image be formed?

c) Is the image real or virtual? Explain your answer.

d) Is the image upright or inverted?

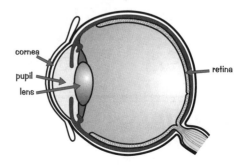

Optical Devices

Q5   The diagrams below show light entering two eyeballs.

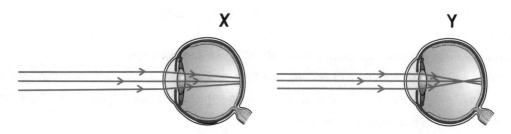

X   Y

a) Which eye needs a convex (converging) lens in front of it in order to focus the light sharply? Explain your answer.

b) Which eye needs a concave (diverging) lens in front of it in order to focus the light sharply? Explain your answer.

c) The lens in eye X is working properly. Is the eyeball too short or too long?

d) The lens in eye Y is working properly. Is the eyeball too short or too long?

Q6   The diagram shows an overhead projector (OHP) being used to focus light from an object onto a screen. It uses a flat mirror to direct the light so that the screen can be on the wall. The head containing the lens and the mirror can be moved up and down.

Copy out these sentences, using the correct word from the brackets.

a) The lens being used in the OHP is (**concave / convex**).

People at the back of the room complain that the writing on the screen is too small to read.

b) To make the image larger, the OHP should be moved (**away from / towards**) the screen.

c) To make the new image sharper, the head should be moved (**down towards / up away from**) the object.

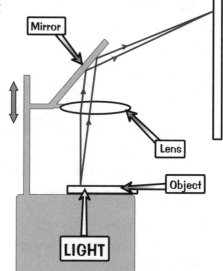

_he he he..._

Top Tips...

OK. First make sure you know the difference between convex and concave. It's the con<u>cave</u> one that <u>caves</u> in the middle... And don't get confused about <u>virtual images</u> — the real object not being there doesn't make it virtual — it's virtual if light doesn't come from where the image is (like behind the mirror).

Resonance

Q1 Copy and complete the paragraph using the words below.
(You can use the words in the box once, more than once, or not at all.)

Every object has its own _____ frequency — this is the number of times it will _____
in a _____ if it is given _____ and left to vibrate. If a driving oscillator tries to force
an object to vibrate, the transfer of _____ will be greatest when the driving frequency
is _____ the natural frequency. When this happens, _____ is occurring and the
amplitude of vibration is _____. At driving frequencies higher and lower than the
natural frequency the amplitude of vibration is _____.

> equal to   second   less than   large
> energy   small   natural   vibrate   resonance

Q2 A hacksaw blade (springy strip of steel) has a small mass glued to one end.
The other end is fixed to a desk. A piece of wire is attached near to the
bottom of the blade and to a vibration generator.

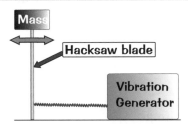

a) The vibration generator has a dial marked in Hertz. Explain what 5 Hz means.

b) The vibration generator is switched off. Explain how you could find the natural frequency (in
Hertz) of the hacksaw blade to a reasonable degree of accuracy.

c) How could you measure the amplitude of vibration of the blade?

*The vibration generator is switched on and the amplitude of the vibration of
the hacksaw blade is recorded. The table below shows the results:*

Frequency (Hz)	1	2	3	4	5	6	7
Amplitude (cm)	2	4	8	5	3	2	1

d) Draw a graph of the results, joining the points with a smooth curve.

e) Use the graph to find the natural frequency of the hacksaw blade.

*A stiff piece of card is stuck onto the blade. When the blade vibrates the card has a
large air resistance and dissipates a lot of energy. The card does not change the
natural frequency of the blade. The experiment is repeated.*

f) On your graph from **d)**, draw the curve you would expect to get from this second experiment.

g) How would making the mass on the blade larger affect the natural frequency?

Q3 Below is a trombone. It's basically a long air-filled brass tube that winds
around in various squiggles. One part of the tube is in a U shape (the coloured
bit), and can be moved back and forth to change the length of the tube.

Draw a rough diagram of the trombone, and add an
arrow to show which direction the player should move
the U shape in order to play a lower pitched note.
Explain your answer in terms of resonance.

Modes of Vibration

Q1   A stretched string is shown below. It is 100 cm long.

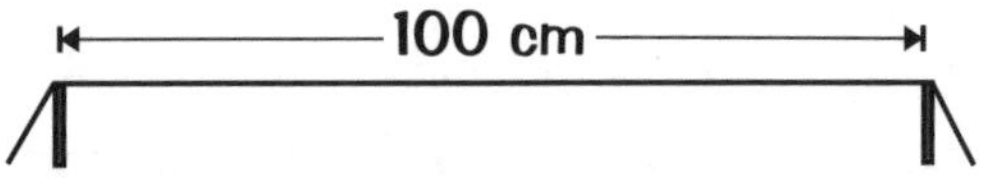

← —————— 100 cm —————— →

a) Sketch the pattern produced by the string vibrating at the fundamental frequency.

b) What is the wavelength (in metres) of the fundamental vibration for this string?

c) Calculate the fundamental frequency if the speed of the waves in the string is 250 m/s.
   Use the formula below.

Frequency = Speed/Wavelength

Q2   The pattern for the second harmonic in a particular stretched string
is shown below. The frequency of this harmonic is 500 Hz.

a) Copy the diagram and add labels to show where the
   nodes are.

b) How does the string move at the nodes?

c) What is the fundamental frequency for this string?

d) i)   Draw the pattern formed by the **fourth** harmonic.

   ii) What is its frequency?

   iii) How many nodes are there?

   iv) How many wavelengths fit onto the string?

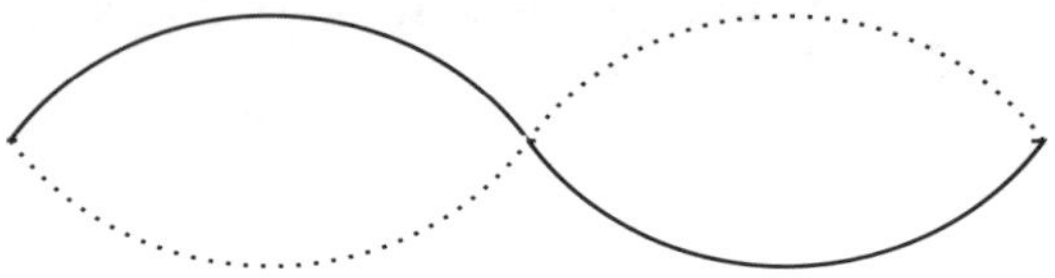

F = 500 Hz

Q3   A microphone attached to an oscilloscope records the sounds produced by
different instruments. All of the instruments are playing the same fundamental note.

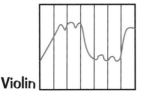 Violin   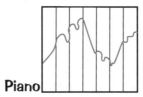 Piano   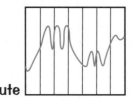 Flute

a) How can you tell that they are all playing the same fundamental note?

b) Even though they are all playing the same fundamental note, the instruments
   sound different and the traces look different. Explain this observation.

Q4   A string is stretched by hanging weights on one end as shown in the diagram. The string is stretched
over two moveable supports R and S. When the string is plucked between R and S, it plays a note.

R   S

a) What happens to the frequency and pitch of the note
   if more weight is hung on the end? Explain your answer.

b) What can be done with support S if a lower note is required? Explain your answer.

c) In what other way can the pitch of the note be changed?

Interference of Waves

Q1 Copy and complete the following paragraph using the words below.

When two waves arrive at the same point they _____. If the waves are in phase (crest meets _____) then _____ interference occurs, and the amplitude of the resulting wave is the _____ of the amplitude of the two waves. If the waves are half a cycle out of phase (crest meets _____) then _____ interference occurs and the amplitude of the resulting wave is the _____ of the amplitudes of the two waves. Two waves, coming from the same source, that have travelled different routes before they meet are said to have a path difference. If the path difference is _____ then destructive interference will occur. If the path difference is either _____ or _____ then constructive interference will occur.

constructive	destructive	crest	zero	half a wavelength
trough	difference	sum	one wavelength	interfere

Q2 Microwaves can show interference effects. Microwaves are partly reflected by wood and totally reflected by metal. The microwave emitter sends out microwaves towards a wooden sheet and a metal sheet. The reflections meet and interfere at the detector. The metal sheet can be moved backwards. The wavelength of the microwaves is 3 cm.

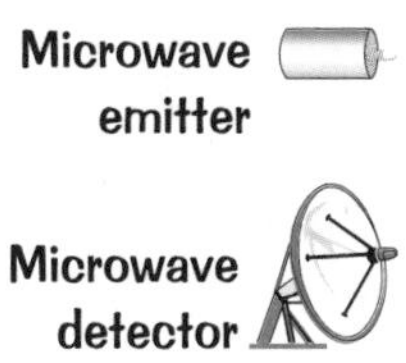

Microwave emitter

Microwave detector

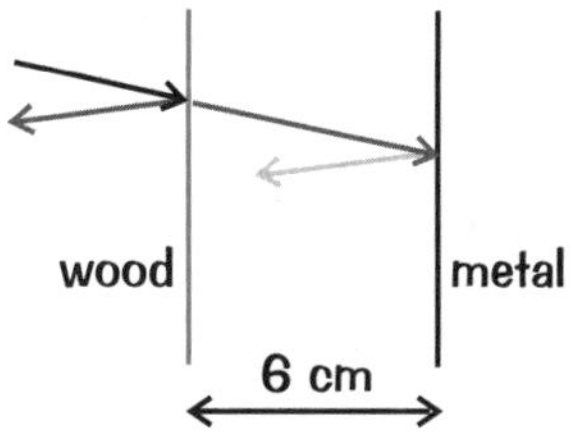

wood   metal

6 cm

a) How much further have the microwaves that have reflected off the metal sheet travelled than those that have reflected off the wooden sheet? What is the name given to this distance?

b) How many wavelengths fit into this distance?

c) Will there be constructive or destructive interference at the detector? Will the amplitude at the detector be at a maximum or a minimum? Explain your answers.

The metal sheet is moved slowly back, away from the detector.

d) Describe what would happen to the amplitude at the detector. Explain your answer.

e) How far does the metal sheet move between each position of maximum amplitude at the detector?

Q3 A vibration generator drives two dippers (A and B) that produce circular water waves of equal amplitude and period. The diagram shows the situation at a particular instant from above — the lines represent crests.

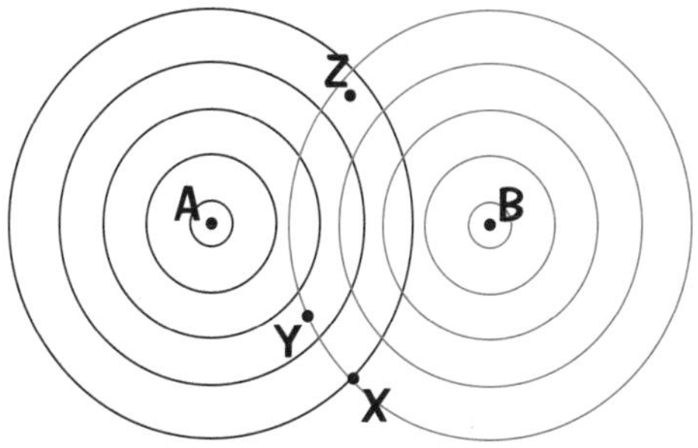

a) What is the name given to the part of the wave half way between each pair of crests?

b) What kind of interference is occurring at point X? What will be seen at X?

c) What kind of interference is occurring at point Y? What will be seen at Y?

d) What kind of interference is occurring at point Z? What will be seen at Z?

e) The period of the waves is one second. What will be seen at Y in two seconds time? Explain your answer.

Z

A   B

Y

X

Section Eight — Communications and Waves

Temperature and Pressure in Gases

Q1   Copy and complete the following paragraph choosing the correct words from the box below.

The Celsius temperature scale has two fixed points. One is the melting point of _____ at

_____. The other is the boiling point of _____ at _____.

The Kelvin temperature scale has one of its fixed points at the lowest temperature possible —

called _____ zero. This is given a value of _____ and it is equivalent to a temperature on

the Celsius scale of about _____. This is the temperature at which the internal _____ of

any substance is at the lowest possible value. To convert from °C to Kelvin you must _____

273. When a gas is heated, the particles in it move _____. The average _____ energy of

particles in a gas is proportional to the temperature of the gas on the _____ scale.

add	faster	subtract	0 °C	energy
ice	kinetic		0 K	100 °C
-273 °C	absolute	Kelvin	water	

Q2   Convert the following temperatures to kelvins (K).

  a) 3 °C   **b)** 210 °C   **c)** -45 °C   **d)** 0 °C

Q3   Convert the following temperatures to °C.

  a) 0 K   **b)** 300 K   **c)** 640 K   **d)** 30 K

Q4   A scuba diving cylinder contains pure oxygen. There is a pressure gauge on the top that reads
        1×10^6 N/m². The gas is at a temperature of 300 K. Another cylinder contains pure hydrogen
        gas that is also at 300 K. An oxygen molecule is much larger than a hydrogen molecule.

  a) Explain in detail why a gas exerts a pressure on the walls of the container.

  b) What can you say about the average kinetic energy of a molecule of the
        oxygen and of a molecule of the hydrogen? Explain your answer.

  The oxygen is heated to a temperature of 600 K.

  Assume it is an ideal gas so: $\dfrac{\text{pressure} \times \text{volume}}{\text{temperature (K)}} = \text{constant.}$

  c) Explain in detail why the pressure of the gas will rise.

  d) Calculate the new reading on the pressure gauge.

Q5   A bubble of carbon dioxide leaves a plant at the bottom of a deep lake and rises to
        the surface. Initially it has a volume of 5 cm³ and is at a pressure of 6 atmospheres.
        The temperature at the bottom of the lake is 4 °C. Just before it reaches the surface
        it is at a pressure of 1 atmosphere and a temperature of 20 °C.

  a) Convert both temperatures to Kelvin.

  b) Give two reasons why the volume of the bubble will increase as it rises.

  c) Calculate the volume of the bubble just before it reaches the surface.

Particles in Atoms

Q1 *During a famous experiment alpha particles were fired at thin gold foil. Detectors were used to determine where the alpha particles went. Some particles were scattered through very large angles.*

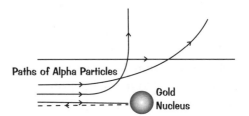

a) What is an alpha particle?
What is the charge on an alpha particle?

b) In what area were most of the alpha particles detected?

c) Were large angle scatters rare or common?

d) What did scientists conclude about the structure of gold from these observations?

Paths of Alpha Particles

Gold Nucleus

Q2 Which of the following are fundamental particles?

Proton	Electron	Neutron
Monkey	Positron	Alpha particle

Q3 Determine which of the following statements are true and which are false. Write each false statement correctly.

a) Protons and electrons have the same charge.

b) A positron has the same mass as an electron.

c) A neutron will repel a positron.

d) There are 2 quarks in a proton.

e) There are 2 types of quark in a neutron.

f) The 3 quarks in a neutron have charges $+\frac{2}{3}$, $-\frac{1}{3}$ and $-\frac{1}{3}$.

g) When a neutron changes into a proton, a $+\frac{2}{3}$ (up) quark changes to a $-\frac{1}{3}$ (down) quark.

h) An electron is made up of 2 quarks and a positron is made up of 3 quarks.

Q4 Copy and complete the paragraph below choosing the correct word in brackets.

During β- decay [**a proton** / **a neutron** / **an electron**] in the nucleus becomes [**a proton** / **a neutron** / **an electron**]. Also released during this process is a high energy [**electron** / **positron** / **quark**] called a β- particle.

During β+ decay [**a proton** / **a neutron** / **an electron**] in the nucleus becomes [**a proton** / **a neutron** / **an electron**]. Also released during this process is a high energy [**electron** / **positron** / **quark**] called a β+ particle.

Top Tips...

It's pretty hard to get your head around these quarks. Just remember, if you add up the charges on the quarks in a neutron you get zero, and if you add up the charges on the quarks in a proton you get +1. Quarks are also fundamental particles — this means you can't divide them into anything smaller.

68

Radioactive Decay

Q1 The graph on the right (of the number of protons, Z, against the number of neutrons, N) shows the line of stability for nuclei.
Most isotopes on this line do not undergo radioactive decay, as they have a combination of protons and neutrons that is stable.

a) What are "isotopes" of an element?

b) Would you describe isotopes in region A as stable or unstable?

c) Are isotopes in region A neutron-rich or proton-rich? (i.e. do they have too many neutrons or protons?)

d) Isotopes in region B are unstable. Suggest a reason for this, referring to the number of protons.

e) In order to achieve stability, what type of decay will isotopes in region B undergo?

f) What type of decay will isotopes in region C undergo in order to achieve stability?

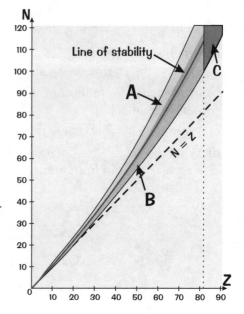

Q2 Copy and complete the sentences by choosing the correct words/numbers from the box below. (You can use each answer more than once.)

| decreases by 1 | increases by 1 | element | 2 | 4 | proton |
| gamma ray | neutron | atomic | stays the same | | |

a) During alpha particle decay, the nucleus loses _____ protons and _____ neutrons. Therefore its mass number decreases by _____ and its atomic number decreases by _____.

b) During β- decay a _____ becomes a _____. The atomic number _____ and the mass number _____.

c) During β+ decay a _____ becomes a _____. The atomic number _____ and the mass number _____.

d) Alpha, β+ or β- decay results in the formation of a different _____ because the _____ number changes.

e) β+ and β- decay is often accompanied by the emission of more energy in the form of a _____ as the nucleus undergoes rearrangement.

Q3 Copy the following decay reactions. Then fill in the missing mass and atomic numbers, and identify the element X.

a)
$$^{228}_{90}\text{Th} \longrightarrow \, ^{?}_{?}\text{Ra} + \, ^{4}_{2}\alpha$$ *Alpha particle*

b)
$$^{?}_{?}\text{X} \longrightarrow \, ^{234}_{91}\text{Pa} + \, ^{0}_{-1}\text{e}$$ *β⁻ particle*

c)
$$^{?}_{84}\text{Po} \longrightarrow \, ^{207}_{?}\text{Bi} + \, ^{0}_{+1}\text{e}$$ *β⁺ particle*

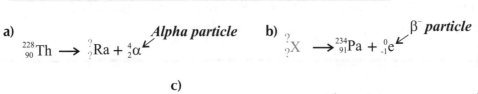

Two weeks after falling into the radioactive waste, Ken began decaying at an alarming rate

Nuclear Fission

Q1 *The atomic number of uranium is 92. When a nucleus of uranium-235 absorbs a neutron it quickly splits into two daughter nuclei and releases several particles. This splitting of an atom is called nuclear fission.*

   a) How many protons are there in a uranium-235 nucleus?

   b) How many neutrons are there in a uranium-235 nucleus?

   c) What isotope of uranium is formed when the neutron is absorbed?

   d) What are the single particles released when the uranium-236 nucleus splits into two daughter nuclei?

   e) A great deal of energy is released during nuclear fission. In what form does this energy appear immediately after the uranium nucleus splits?

Q2 The diagram on the right shows a uranium-235 nucleus absorbing a neutron and undergoing fission to release 3 neutrons (the daughter nuclei formed are not shown).

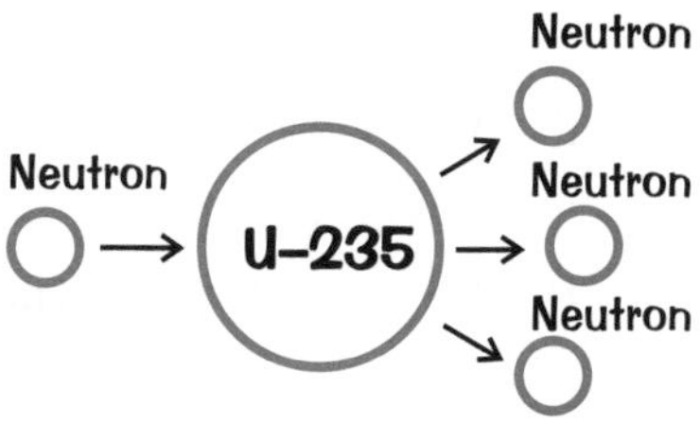

   a) Copy the diagram and add to it to illustrate how a chain reaction can occur in a lump of uranium-235.

   b) In terms of energy, what is the result of a chain reaction?

   c) In what device would a chain reaction be used?

   d) When nuclear fission is used in a power station as a source of energy, the chain reaction must be controlled. Explain why?

   e) In the reactor core of a nuclear power station, control rods usually absorb 2 out of every 3 neutrons released during a fission.

     i) What effect will this have on the chain reaction?

     ii) The control rods can be adjusted so that they absorb all of the released neutrons. What effect does this have on the chain reaction?

Diagram labels: Neutron → U-235 → Neutron, Neutron, Neutron

Q3 One possible result of the fission of a uranium-235 nucleus is shown in the equation below:

$$^{235}_{92}U + {}^{1}_{0}n \longrightarrow {}^{145}_{\text{i)}\_}X + {}^{\text{ii)}\_}_{38}Z + 3{}^{1}_{0}n$$

   a) Copy the equation and complete it by filling in the missing atomic and mass numbers.

   b) How would you use a Periodic Table to identify the elements X and Y?

Q4 Say which of the following statements about electricity generation are true. Correct any that you think are false.

   a) A nuclear power station contains a turbine and a generator.

   b) Nuclear power stations release gases responsible for acid rain.

   c) Nuclear power stations do not release carbon dioxide.

   d) Radioactive waste from a nuclear power station is safe once cooled down.

   e) Nuclear power is renewable.

   f) Radioactive waste from a nuclear power station is safe after a year.

Top Tips...

I went to this power station nearby — they had a new logo. They said it represented better what the power station was. It was a large see-through salmon mounted at the top of the building. Yup... it was a nu-clear-fish-on power station.

Electron Guns

Q1 The diagram on the right shows part of an oscilloscope. The coil carries a large current that causes the cathode to get hot and release particles.

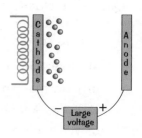

a) What particles are released from the hot cathode? Are they positively or negatively charged?

b) What is the name given to the release of these particles?

c) What is the effect of the high voltage between the cathode and the anode on these particles?

Q2 An electron accelerates across a potential difference (voltage) of 4 kV. The charge on the electron is -1.6×10^{-19} C.

a) Calculate the kinetic energy gained by the electron. (Hint — use the formula triangle below.)

b) How much potential energy will the electron lose? (Hint — think about energy conservation.)

c) The mass of the electron is 9.1×10^{-31} kg. What will be its final speed?

A proton (charge $+1.6 \times 10^{-19}$ C and mass 1.7×10^{-27} kg) accelerates across the same 4 kV potential difference.

d) Explain why the proton will accelerate in the opposite direction to the electron.

e) How much kinetic energy will the proton gain?

f) How does the final speed of the proton compare to that of the electron?

Q3 A beam of electrons leaves an electron gun. The current carried by the beam is 4 mA. The charge on an electron is -1.6×10^{-19} C.

a) How many coulombs of charge pass a certain point in the beam per second?

b) How many electrons pass this point per second?

Q4 The diagram below shows the inside of an oscilloscope. The voltage being measured is applied to the Y plates. The Y plate input is set at 2 V/cm.

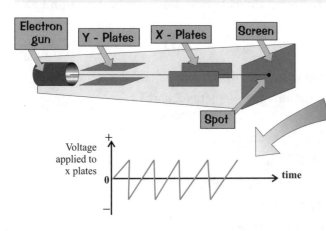

a) If the voltage being measured is 8 V, how far will the spot deflect vertically?

The timebase control on the X-plates is set to 0.1 s/cm. The voltage shown on this graph is then applied to the X-plates.

b) Explain why the voltage pattern applied to the X plates will cause the spot to move across the screen from left to right and then jump back to the left and start again.

c) The 'timebase' control adjusts how quickly the spot moves across the screen. How would the graph on the left change if the time-base was set at 0.2 s/cm?

d) *The diagram on the right shows the screen when an alternating voltage is applied to the Y plates. The input is set at 2 V/cm and the time-base is set at 0.1 s/cm. Calculate:*

i) the amplitude,

ii) the period,

iii) the frequency.

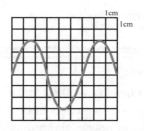

Lower the oscilloscope and then dive, dive, dive...

Electronic Systems

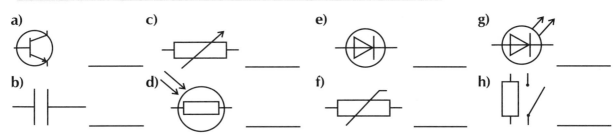

Q1 Match the following symbols with their names from the list below.

a) _____   c) _____   e) _____   g) _____

b) _____   d) _____   f) _____   h) _____

| LED | thermistor | transistor | variable resistor |
| relay (normally open) | | capacitor | LDR | diode |

Q2 Copy and complete the table below, using the words in the box.
Classify the components as input sensors, processors or output transducers.

| thermistor | buzzer | AND gate | NOT gate | transistor | LED |
| LDR | magnetic switch | pressure switch | motor | heater | OR gate |

Input Sensors	Processors	Output Transducers

Q3 The diagram below shows the internal mechanism of a relay.

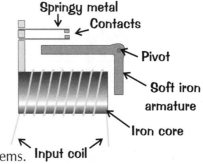

a) What is created by the coil when a current flows through it?

b) What effect does this have on the soft iron armature?

c) Draw a diagram to show what this does to the contacts.

d) Why is this type of relay often called a 'normally open' relay?

e) Draw a possible design for a 'normally closed' relay.

f) Give two reasons why relays are often included in electronic systems.

Q4 The symbol opposite represents a transistor.

a) What is the name given to connection X?

b) What is the name given to connection Y?

c) What is the name given to connection Z?

d) What does the transistor allow when a large enough voltage is at connection X?

Top Tips...

Before you leave this section — learn the symbols. Very important. And remember — __input__ sensors
give signals to __processors__ that give instructions to __output__ devices.

Logic Gates

Q1 The diagram below shows a system containing a logic gate and an LED.

State the approximate voltage of the
output of the logic gate when it is:
a) logic 1
b) logic 0

State and explain what will happen to the
LED when the output of the logic gate is:
c) logic 1
d) logic 0

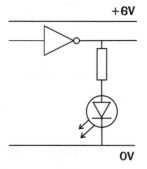

+6V

0V

Q2 The inputs and outputs of logic gates can be shown concisely in truth tables.

Complete the truth tables for the following logic gates.

a) Input ▷ Output

Input	Output
0	
1	

b) A, B → Output

A B	Output
0 0	
0 1	
1 0	
1 1	

c) A, B → Output

A B	Output
0 0	
0 1	
1 0	
1 1	

Draw the symbol and name the single logic gates responsible for the following truth tables.

d)

A B	Output
0 0	0
0 1	1
1 0	1
1 1	1

e)

A B	Output
0 0	1
0 1	1
1 0	1
1 1	0

Alfred the gate.

Q3 A combination of logic gates is shown below.

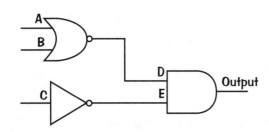

A B C	D E	Output
0 0 0		
0 0 1		
0 1 0		
1 0 0		
1 1 0		
1 0 1		
0 1 1		
1 1 1		

a) Copy and complete the truth table.
b) Summarise the action of the combination e.g. "The output is logic 1 if ...."

Using Logic Gates

Q1 Replace each of the logic gate combinations below with a single equivalent logic gate.

a)    b) 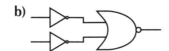   c)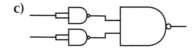

Q2 A sports car has two doors. It is dangerous if one of the doors is opened while the handbrake is off. A warning buzzer should sound if this happens.
The door sensors are at logic 1 when closed and logic 0 when open. The handbrake sensor is at logic 1 when off and logic 0 when on. The door sensors are marked A and B, H is the handbrake sensor and the output to the warning buzzer is C.

a) Which of the following combinations would be a suitable system for the car?

i) 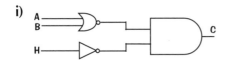   ii)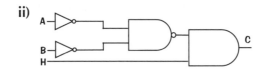

iii)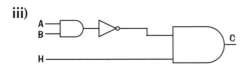

b) For each of the other combinations explain at least one situation in which the system fails to meet the requirements.

Q3 The diagram below shows a pretty nasty looking arrangement of logic gates.

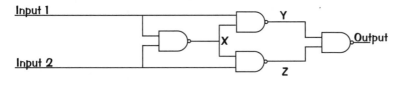

Input 1	Input 2	X	Y	Z	Output
0	0				
0	1				
1	0				
1	1				

a) Copy and complete the truth table opposite.

b) How would you describe the action of this combination?

Q4 For each of the following situations, use combinations of logic gates to make a system that satisfies the requirements.

a) An engineer wants to construct a safety system for a circular saw machine. The machine must only come on if the safety guard is down (1 when down), the user is standing on a pressure pad (1 when standing on it) and the main switch is on (1 when on).

b) A warning light should come on if a baby's nappy is wet (1 when wet) and he is crying (1 when crying), or if his brother opens his bedroom door (1 when shut).

Using Logic Gates

Q5 The circuit below shows a burglar alarm. The alarm sounds if a burglar steps on a pressure pad (1 when standing on it), breaks a light beam (0 if broken) or opens a window (0 when opened). The alarm is only armed when a key is turned.

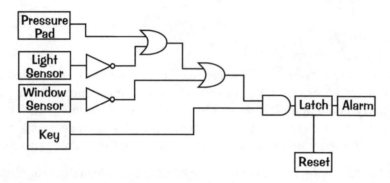

a) What is the purpose of the latch and the reset button?

b) Draw a circuit diagram of a latch using two NOR gates.

c) Explain how your latch works — describe the inputs and outputs of the gates:
   (i) when the alarm is initially armed (and the output is off),
   (ii) when the alarm is triggered (e.g. when someone treads on the pressure pad),
   (iii) when the person steps off the pressure pad,
   (iv) when the system is reset.

Q6 Look at the combination of logic gates shown below.

Positions in the combination are labelled so that you can refer to them during your explanations. The output starts at 0.

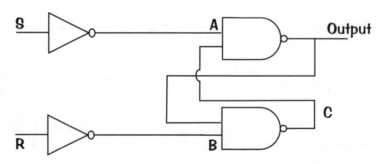

Catherine the gate

a) When S is 0 and R is 0, explain why the output will stay 0.
   (Hint: Start with the bottom *NAND* gate.)

b) Explain what happens to the output when S becomes 1. (R is still 0.)

c) What then happens to the output if S returns to 0? (R is still 0.)

d) What will be the effect of setting R to 1 once S has returned to 0?

e) Explain why the combination behaves as a latch, with S as the input and R as the reset.

Top Tips...

It doesn't get any harder than this at GCSE. My only advice when you're doing this kind of question is to take it nice and slow, and be prepared for it to get a bit frustrating and confusing at certain points along the way. But the good thing is that if you can get your head round latches, you can probably get your head round anything else that's going to be thrown at you during your GCSEs. So hurrah for that.

Potential Dividers

Q1 Calculate the reading on the voltmeter for each of these circuits:

a)

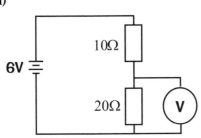

b)

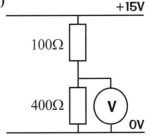

c)

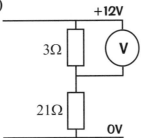

Q2 Study the potential divider below. Then copy and complete the paragraph using the words from the box. You will need to use some words more than once.

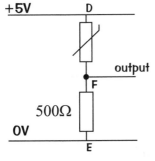

0 V 5 V	potential
thermistor	fixed resistor
very small	very large
hot	cold

THE POTENTIAL DIVIDER

The voltage or _____ difference between points D and E is _____. Initially the thermistor is cold and so its resistance is _____. The majority of the voltage is across the _____ with only a small proportion across the _____. The potential of point F is therefore close to _____. When the temperature of the thermistor is high, its resistance becomes _____. The majority of the voltage is now across the _____ with only a small proportion across the _____. The potential of point F will now be close to _____. This potential divider can be said to give an output of logic 1 when the thermistor is _____ and an output of logic 0 when the thermistor is _____. Changing the value of the _____ can control the temperature at which the output changes from 1 to 0.

Q3 Calculate the potential of point X in each of these potential dividers:

a)

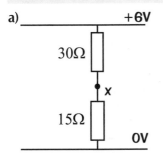

b)

c)

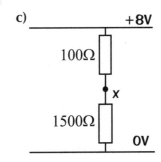

Top Tips...

You've got the *potential* to get a heap of marks here. *Divide* it up — learn the equation, then learn how to use it. (Sorry about the pun, it just jumped onto the page... I tried to hold it back... I did... maybe I'm working too hard...)

Section Ten — Control in Circuits

Capacitors

Q1   Initially the capacitor in the circuit below is uncharged. The switch is then
moved to position A. After some time the switch is moved to position B.
Use the words in the box to complete the paragraph below.

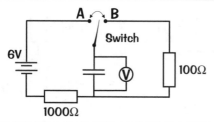

charged	charge	discharged
	current	0 V	6 V
discharge	resistance	greater
	rises	falls	smaller

When the switch is moved to position A, a _____ flows from the battery and the
capacitor begins to _____. The reading on the voltmeter is initially _____ and
then it _____. When the reading on the voltmeter is equal to _____ it stops
changing. The capacitor is now fully _____. When the switch is moved to position
B, the capacitor begins to _____. The voltmeter reading _____ until it is equal to
_____. The capacitor is now fully _____. The discharging occurs more quickly
than the charging because the _____ of the discharge circuit is _____.

Q2   Look at the circuit and graph below. The graph shows how the reading
on the voltmeter changes with time, when the switch is closed.

Copy the graph and add lines to
represent the following changes:

a) The resistance is increased.

b) The capacitance is decreased.

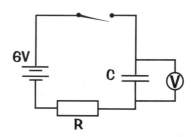

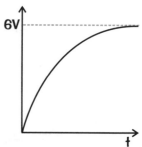

Q3   Frederick is afraid of the hairy three-eyed sludge monster that appears at the bottom of
his bed when it's dark. His one defence is a night-light that he can switch on if he wakes
up in the middle of the night. He usually falls asleep again very quickly, so a capacitor
in the night-light acts as a timer to switch the light off automatically after a certain time.

a) Before the switch is pressed the capacitor is charged and
the potential of point P is 5 V. Explain why the light is off.

b) Explain why the capacitor is quickly discharged when the
switch is pressed.

c) The switch is pressed and released and the capacitor is
discharged. Explain why the light comes on.

d) A current now flows from A to B. What effect does this
have on the capacitor and on the potential of point P?
Why does the light switch off after a time?

e) Suggest two ways in which the circuit can be changed in
order to lengthen the time for which the light stays on.

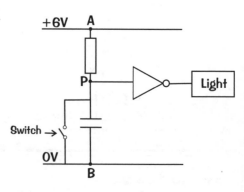

Section Ten — Control in Circuits

Electronic Systems in Practice

Q1 An electronic system is shown below. It can be used as a light dependent switch.

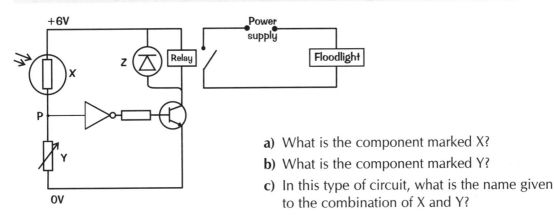

a) What is the component marked X?

b) What is the component marked Y?

c) In this type of circuit, what is the name given to the combination of X and Y?

d) Give three ways in which the potential of point P can be changed.

Component X is in bright light.

e) Is its resistance very high or very low?

f) What roughly is the potential of P when X is in bright light?

g) What is the output of the NOT gate?

h) Does the transistor allow current to flow through the relay?

i) Does the floodlight come on?

j) What is device Z? What is its purpose?

Physics puts LED in your pencil.

k) Copy and complete the paragraph below using some of the following words.

not come on	0	6V	will not	will
1	0V	come on	high	low

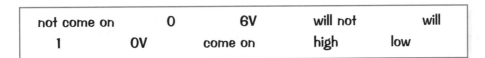

When component X is in dark conditions its resistance is _____, which means that the potential of point P is about _____. This means that the output of the NOT gate is _____. The transistor _____ allow current through the relay. This means that the floodlight will _____.

l) Suggest what would happen if component X was placed directly in front of the floodlight.

m) It is found that this light dependent switch system is switching the floodlight on and off at the wrong light level. How can the circuit be adjusted to alter the light level at which the floodlight comes on?

n) What changes would you make to the circuit above to create a system that would make a motor open some blinds when it is light outside?

o) What changes would you make to the circuit above to create a system that would turn a heater on when it is cold?

Q2 It has been said that what divides more developed countries from those in the less developed countries is "the availability of and fast access to information". Discuss this comment with reference to the role of electronic systems.

Stretching Things

Q1 The graph below shows the extension of a spring when an increasing force is applied.

a) What type of behaviour is the spring showing in region X?

b) What type of behaviour is the spring showing in region Y?

c) What is the name given to the point Z?

d) What is the relationship between force and extension in region X?

e) The spring is stretched to point P. Explain what the spring will do when the force is gradually removed.

f) The spring is stretched to point Q. Explain what the spring will do when the force is gradually removed.

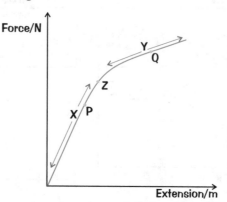

Q2 Copy and complete the following paragraph choosing the correct words from the brackets.

> The spring constant of a spring can be determined by applying
> **(a force / an extension / a banana / energy)** and measuring the **(peel / extension / mass / energy)**
> as long as the **(plastic / elastic)** limit has not been reached. The spring constant can then be
> calculated by dividing **(force / extension / mass / energy)** by the
> **(force / extension / mass / energy)**. The units of a spring constant are
> **(newtons / metres / kilograms / joules)** per **(newton / metre / kilogram / joule)**.
> A large spring constant indicates that the spring is **(hard / easy)** to stretch.

Q3 A force of 40 N stretches a spring of unstretched length 20 cm. It is now 30 cm long.
When the force is removed the spring returns to a length of 20 cm. Calculate:

a) the spring constant,

b) the energy stored in the spring when its length is 30 cm.

$$\text{energy stored (J)} = \frac{\text{force (N)} \times \text{extension (m)}}{2}$$

Q4 A cable supports a lift. The cable is 50 m long when the lift is empty.
Every time a crate is put into the lift, the cable gets longer. Each crate weighs 1000 N.

Weight of crates/N	0	1000	2000	3000	4000	5000	6000	7000
Length/m	50.0	50.5	51.1	50.8	52.0	52.5	54.0	55.5
Extension/m	0							

a) Copy and complete the table.

b) Plot a graph of force against extension. (Extension on the x-axis).

c) There is one reading that was anomalous. Mark this on your graph.

d) What would be the length of the cable if 7 people got in, each weighing 500 N?

e) Calculate the spring constant of the cable in N/m.
(Hint: work out the gradient of the initial part of the graph)

f) Mark the elastic limit of the cable on your graph.

g) What is the energy stored in the cable due to 5 crates being in the lift?
(Hint: you can calculate energy stored using the formula above, or from the area under the graph).

h) What can you say about the length of the cable when the 7 crates are taken out of the lift?

Centre of Mass and Stability

Q1   Calculate the density of the following objects.

a) A brick, mass 2 kg and volume 0.001 m³.
b) Foam packaging, mass 4 kg and volume 0.5 m³.
c) A tree trunk, mass 1500 kg and volume 3 m³.
d) The block of iron on the right.

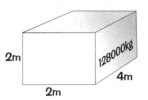

Q2   A block of a new super metal called Densitonium has a mass of 500 g and a volume of 55 cm³.

$$1 \text{ m}^3 = 1000000 \text{ cm}^3,$$
$$1 \text{ tonne} = 1000 \text{ kg}$$

a) What is the density of Densitonium?
b) What would be the volume of a 2.3 tonne block of Densitonium?

Q3   Some double-decker buses have signs asking people to sit upstairs only if the downstairs seats are full. Explain why, referring to stability in your answer.

Q4   A student is using a retort stand to do an experiment involving hanging weights on a rubber band. Which of the following arrangements would be most stable? Explain your answer.

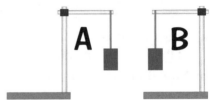

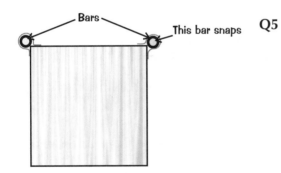

Q5   Two smooth bars support a square sheet of wood by passing through small metal loops attached to the two top corners of the sheet. One of the bars snaps, leaving the sheet freely pivoted at one corner.

a) Explain why the sheet begins to rotate.
b) Where will the sheet eventually come to rest?

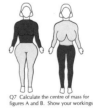

Q7 Calculate the centre of mass for figures A and B. Show your workings.

Q6   Fill in the gaps using the words from the box to describe a method for finding where the centre of mass of a flat shape lies.

plumb line	different	cross	mass	line

Freely suspend the shape, and hang a _____ from the point of suspension as well. Draw a _____ down the plumb line. Then do the same thing again, but suspend the shape from a _____ point on its surface. The centre of _____ is where the two lines _____.

Top Tips...

Using the density equation is a doddle as long as you put everything in the correct <u>units</u> — mass in <u>kg</u> and volume in <u>m³</u>. As far as stability goes, just remember that the most stable objects have a <u>wide base</u> and a <u>low centre of mass</u>, and that things topple over if the <u>line of action</u> passes outside the <u>base</u>.

Moments

Q1   Explain the following.

a) A door handle is placed on the opposite side to the hinges.

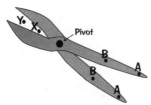

b) To cut very strong steel wire, you should:
   i)   push with your hands at position A rather than position B.
   ii) put the wire at position X rather than position Y.

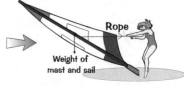

c) The windsurfer will need to pull on the rope with a large force to start lifting the mast and sail in the position shown.

d) When sailing a yacht in high winds, sailors will often lean over one side of the boat. (It isn't because they're feeling a bit sick. Well, not usually.)

Q2   A 6 m long ladder is resting (but not balanced) on a gate 1m from its end. The ladder weighs 400 N.

a) Bob holds one end of the ladder. What is the size and direction of the force that he must exert to keep the ladder horizontal?

b) Now Bob lets go, and Bill stands at the other end of the ladder. What is the size and direction of the force that he must exert to keep the ladder horizontal?

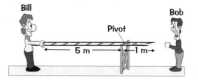

Q3   A rope is attached to the end of a barrier of weight 900 N. This end is lying on the floor but the other is attached to a pivot as shown in the diagram. The rope pulls vertically. (The barrier is a uniform shape and density.)

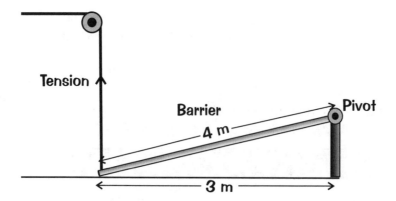

a) Copy the diagram and show the weight of the barrier acting at its centre of mass.

b) What is the anticlockwise moment exerted by the weight of the barrier about the pivot?

c) What clockwise moment must the tension in the rope exert in order to hold the barrier just off the floor?

d) What is the tension in the rope when this happens?

e) If the rope would break if the tension in it were 440 N, how can the rope still be used to hold the barrier off the floor? Explain your answer.

Momentum and Collisions

Q1 Which of the following are vector quantities?

 Velocity Momentum Speed Direction Distance

Q2 Calculate the momentum of these objects:

a) A dog of mass 25 kg running at 7 m/s.

b) A car of mass 1500 kg moving at 15 m/s.

c) A spider of mass 2 g moving at 2 cm/s.

Q3 Two 'rugby on ice' players skate directly towards each other. Player A has a mass of 120 kg and skates at a speed of 6 m/s and player B has a mass of 80 kg and moves at a speed of 4 m/s. Positive is to the right.

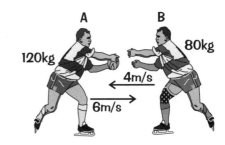

a) What is the momentum of player A?

b) What is the momentum of player B?

c) What is the total momentum of the two players before the collision?

d) What is the total momentum of the two players after the collision?

e) When they collide the two players grab hold of each other and stick together. At what velocity will they move after the collision?

Q4 A train engine of mass 10 000 kg is travelling at a speed of 8 m/s towards a carriage of mass 4000 kg that is travelling in the same direction at 3 m/s. When they collide they couple together.

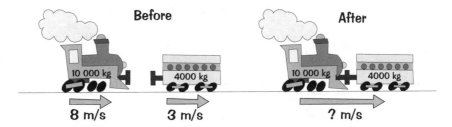

a) What is the momentum of the engine before the collision?

b) What is the momentum of the carriage before the collision?

c) What is the total momentum of the carriage and the engine before the collision?

d) What is the total momentum of the carriage and the engine after the collision?

e) At what speed do they move off together?

f) How much momentum has the engine lost?

g) How much momentum has the carriage gained?

Momentum and Collisions

Q5 A curling stone (curling's a bit like bowling on ice) of mass 6 kg moves at 5 m/s towards a stationary stone of mass 10 kg. They collide head on and the smaller stone rebounds backwards at a speed of 1 m/s. At what speed will the larger stone move off?

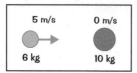

Drawing diagrams like this can often help.

Q6 A helicopter hovers above the ground. The rotor blades push air downwards. During a period of 30 seconds a total of 36 000 kg of air is pushed downwards at a speed of 10 m/s.

a) What was the total change of momentum of the air? (Assume the air was still to start with.)

b) What was the force acting on the air?

c) What is the weight of the helicopter? Explain your answer.

d) If the helicopter needs to accelerate upwards, what action can the pilot take? Explain your answer.

$$\text{Force acting (N)} = \frac{\text{Change in momentum (kgm/s)}}{\text{Time taken for change to happen (s)}}$$

Q7 Complete the following paragraphs using the words in the box.

time	large	longer
smaller	short	momentum

If a parachutist lands without bending her knees she will change her momentum over a _____ time. This will mean a _____ force acts. If she does bend her legs she will change her momentum over a _____ time, which means a _____ force will act.

A tennis player 'follows through' with a shot so that the racket is in contact with the ball for a longer _____, allowing a larger overall change in _____ of the ball.

Top Tips...

There's plenty of practice at working out momentum here. It's easy to bung the numbers into the formula but the tricky bit is remembering that momentum has direction — so you have to decide which way is positive before you start. If you don't, you're going to end up in a bit of a muddle.

Section Eleven — Mechanics

Equations of Motion

$$s = \frac{(u+v)t}{2} \qquad v = u + at \qquad s = ut + \frac{1}{2}at^2 \qquad v^2 = u^2 + 2as$$

Q1 A cyclist starts from rest and accelerates at a constant 2.5 m/s² for 4 seconds.

a) What is the final speed of the cyclist?

b) How far did the cyclist travel during the 4 seconds?

Q2 A bus travelling at an initial speed of 8 m/s accelerates uniformly at 3 m/s² until it reaches a speed of 20 m/s.

a) How long does the acceleration take?

b) How far does the bus travel during this time?

Q3 A horse is travelling at an initial speed of 2 m/s and accelerates uniformly at 2 m/s² for a distance of 40 m.

a) What is the final speed reached at the end of the 40 m?

b) How long did the horse take to cover the 40 m?

Q4 A car travelling at an initial speed of 30 m/s starts to brake, coming to a complete stop in 10 s. The deceleration is uniform.

a) What is the value of the deceleration?

b) How far does the car travel during braking?

Q5 A stunt car is driven off the edge of a cliff. It leaves the top of the cliff moving horizontally at a speed of 20 m/s. The cliff is 40 m high. The car accelerates downwards due to gravity at 9.8 m/s². Air resistance and friction can be ignored.

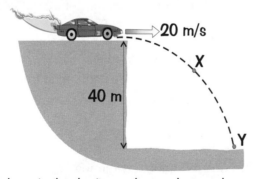

a) What is the initial vertical velocity as the car leaves the top of the cliff?

b) What is the horizontal velocity of the car at point X? Explain your answer.

c) What is the horizontal velocity of the car at point Y (just before impact)?

d) How long will the car take to hit the ground?

e) What is the vertical velocity of the car at point Y (just before impact)?

f) As the car leaves the top of the cliff, it topples a brick over the edge that falls vertically. How long does the brick take to hit the ground? Explain your answer.

Hint — just consider the vertical motion

Circular Motion, SHC and Resistors

I know — it's a bit of a random mix of questions on this page. Well, variety is the spice of life...

Q1 State whether each of these statements is true or false.
Write out a correct version for each false statement.

a) Objects can travel around a circle at a constant velocity.
b) To move in a circle, a car must be constantly accelerating.
c) The centripetal force acts away from the centre of the circle.
d) Increasing the radius of the circle (mass and speed constant) increases the centripetal force needed.
e) If the centripetal force decreases (mass and radius constant), the rotation speed decreases.

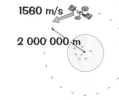
$$\text{centripetal force} = \frac{\text{mass} \times \text{speed}^2}{\text{radius}}$$

Q2 Calculate the centripetal force needed for the following circular motions:

a) i) A car (mass 1000 kg) going around a bend (radius 15 m) at a speed of 12 m/s.

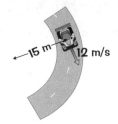

ii) Conker (mass 50 g) being swung in a horizontal circle on a string of length 50 cm at a speed of 3 m/s.

iii) A satellite (mass 500 kg) orbiting the moon at a radius of 2 000 000 m at a speed of 1560 m/s.

b) Copy each of the diagrams above and add an arrow to show the centripetal force acting. For each situation, state what provides the centripetal force needed.

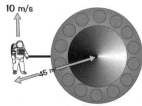

Q3 The spaceship on the left is spinning about its centre. An astronaut of mass 80 kg is held on to the outer edge of the spaceship by a short rope. He is travelling at a constant speed of 10 m/s. He is 45 m from the centre of the spaceship.

a) What is the circumference of the circle that the astronaut is moving in?
b) How long does the astronaut take to do a complete rotation?
c) What is the tension in the rope? (Hint: think about the centripetal force)
d) Copy the diagram and draw on the path that would be taken by the astronaut if the rope were to suddenly snap.

Q4 An electric heater is used to warm up an outdoor swimming pool. The pool contains 500 kg of water and starts off at 12 °C. *(The specific heat capacity of water is 4200J/kg.°C.)*

a) How much energy does it take to increase the temperature of the water by 1 °C?
b) How long will it take (in minutes) to increase the temperature of the water to 40 °C if the heater transfers 20kJ of energy each second?

Q5 A resistor has four bands. The first band is brown, the second is green and the third is orange. The last band is silver.

a) What is the value of this resistor? (Use the table on the right to help you.)
b) What is its tolerance? Calculate the maximum resistance of this resistor.

0	black
1	brown
2	red
3	orange
4	yellow
5	green
6	blue
7	violet
8	grey
9	white